Construction planning

ENGINEERING MANAGEMENT

Series editor S. H. Wearne, BSc(Eng), PhD, FICE, FBIM, Consultant, Director of Institution courses and in-company training

Editorial panel D. E. Neale, CEng, FICE; D. P. Maguire, BSc, FICE; D. J. Ricketts, BSc; B. A. O. Hewett, BSc(Eng), MSc, FICE; J. V. Tagg, CEng, FICE

Other titles in the series

Civil engineering insurance and bonding, P. Madge
Marketing of engineering services, J. B. H. Scanlon
Civil engineering contracts, S. H. Wearne
Managing people, A. S. Martin and F. Grover (Eds)
Management of design offices, P. A. Rutter (Ed)
Control of engineering projects, S. H. Wearne (Ed)
Project evaluation, R. K. Corrie (Ed)
Financial control, N. M. L. Barnes (Ed)

ENGINEERING MANAGEMENT

Construction planning

Richard H. Neale, BSc, MSc, CEng, MICE, MCIOB
David E. Neale, CEng, FICE, MIHT, MBIM

T Thomas Telford, London

Published by Thomas Telford Ltd, Thomas Telford House,
1 Heron Quay, London E14 9XF

First published 1989

  690·0684 NEA

British Library Cataloguing in Publication Data
Neale, R. H.
1. Construction planning. Project management
I. Title II. Neale, D. E.
624'.068'4

ISBN: 0 7277 1322 1

Typeset in Great Britain by MHL Typesetting Limited, Coventry
Printed and bound in Great Britain by Billings & Sons Limited, Worcester

Preface

This guide aims to review construction planning in a simple and practical way. We have been construction project managers, and this is reflected in the style and content of the book. Our aim has been to describe and explain good planning practice which can be applied with diligent but not excessive effort; planning that produces results without protracted analysis and massive computer print-out.

This guide has three parts

- Part 1: Context and strategy
- Part 2: Techniques, procedures and methods
- Part 3: Planning in practice.

In part 1, chapter 1 emphasizes the vital role that managers must play in the planning process, and also introduces some essential preliminary principles. Chapter 2 describes the important strategic decision-making process that lays a practical foundation for an effective plan.

Part 2 is the technical core of the book. Chapters 3–5 describe planning techniques, the planning and management of construction resources, and the techniques and methods of effective control.

Part 3 explains how planning is used in practice. Chapter 6 explains the organization of planning, and the way in which plans are developed and shaped to achieve the best balance of resource usage, timely completion and the economical recovery of overhead costs. Chapter 7 concludes the book with three case studies, which give a detailed illustration of the planning process applied to three actual construction projects.

A simplifying assumption used in the guide has been the use

of the term contractor. Despite the contemporary diversification
of the forms of organizations and contract for civil engineering projects, contractor remains the term which is most commonly used
for those who construct civil engineering works. For the purposes
of the discussion of construction planning, and to simplify the text,
it is also reasonable to regard organizations such as local authority
direct labour forces as contractors. Similarly, all design organizations have been called designers.

Richard Neale
Loughborough University of Technology

David Neale
May Gurney & Co Ltd
Norwich

Acknowledgements

This guide reflects the acquisition of knowledge and experience over a considerable period. During this time, both of the Authors have benefitted from discussions with many successful planners and managers who have been prepared to share and exchange experiences. Grateful thanks are extended to these perceptive and helpful people.

All three case studies in chapter 7 are taken from real life, and the Authors wish to extend their sincere thanks to the clients of these projects for allowing the information to be published. The Authors wished to write a practical book, and this can only be achieved with the inclusion of real information; and this depends on the co-operation of real people.

Several of the staff of May Gurney and Company Ltd helped in the preparation of this guide, and sincere thanks are due to: Jim Holmes, chairman of May Gurney and Company Ltd for permission to use the case study material; Alan Phillips, chief planning engineer, for the computer examples; Peter Foreman and Ron Abbott for advice on linear programmes and monitoring; and Joyce Wilde, Angela Pearce and Christine Hill for the typescript.

Contents

Part 1. Context and strategy

1 **Construction planning in context**   1
   1.1. Planning: the common thread   3
   1.2. The project manager   4
   1.3. Objectives of planning   4
   1.4. Planning and planning techniques   5
   1.5. Planning data   6
   1.6. Planning in the organization   7
   1.7. The cost of planning   8

2 **Early decisions**   10
   2.1. Who is the plan for?   10
   2.2. What should be the level of detail?   10
   2.3. What should be the time-scale?   15
   2.4. The planning hierarchy   15
   2.5. Programme duration   15
   2.6. Activity and activity duration   17
   2.7. Activity duration   18
   2.8. Summary   20

Part 2. Techniques, procedures and methods

3 **Planning techniques**   22
   3.1. The anatomy of planning techniques   22
   3.2. The planner's tool-kit   23
   3.3. Which technique?   25
   3.4. Bar charts   28
   3.5. Line-of-balance   33
   3.6. Linear programmes (time-chainage charts) 44
   3.7. Network analysis   51

4 Resources   **74**
4.1. Estimation of resource requirements   75
4.2. Resource analysis   76
4.3 Other forms of presentation   80
4.4. Planning for effective scheduling   81
4.5. Scheduling systems   83
4.6. Resource scheduling and people-management   83

5 Monitoring and control   **84**
5.1. Control of risk   85
5.2. Client's control   87
5.3. The contract programme   88
5.4. Contractor's control   90
5.5. S-curves: the basic tool   93
5.6. Contractors' control curves   95
5.7. Control curve for progress and cost/value comparison   95
5.8. Cash flow curve   96
5.9. Control curves for labour, plant and equipment   98
5.10. Monitoring progress by key activities and resources   100
5.11. Control of materials   100
5.12. Monitoring line-of-balance and linear programmes   100
5.13. Management information systems   101

Part 3. Planning in practice

6 Putting planning into practice   **103**
6.1. Working space   103
6.2. Initial appraisal   105
6.3. Early decisions   105
6.4. Detailed appraisal   108
6.5. Planning and conferring   110
6.6. Shaping the plan   111
6.7. Variations and project control   119
6.8. Handing over the plan   120
6.9. The dynamics of project management   121
6.10. The changing emphasis of planning   122
6.11. Short-term planning   122
6.12. Summary   124

7 **Case studies** 125
   7.1. Line-of-balance case study 125
   7.2. Linear programme (time-chainage chart) case study 135
   7.3. Network analysis case study 141

References 156

Bibliography 158

Index 159

1 Construction planning in context

> This chapter gives a general review of planning, which is the common thread in construction management. The objectives of planning are explained, and a distinction is made between planning and the use of planning techniques. The important role of the project manager, planning in the organization, and the cost of planning complete a review of the organizational context.

All construction projects require planning and they often require huge expenditure. They usually require their designers and constructors to produce something large and unique over a long timescale, in the open air, in a place where few or even no production facilities exist before the project starts. Any manager who does not plan is no manager: it is a long-established principle that planning is one of the major managerial functions; it is managers who must plan to anticipate and influence future events. Furthermore, managers who do not *plan* cannot *control*, because they have no yardstick by which to judge actual progress or expenditure.

The Authors believe that most experienced civil engineers understand the paramount importance of planning, and few underestimate how difficult it can be to do it effectively. This guide aims to assist in making planning effective. The major aspects of construction planning will be reviewed, the techniques explained and some practical case studies for illustrations given. Unfortunately, no guide can provide the two factors most crucial to effective planning

- commitment of the senior management to making the planning function work effectively, and to gaining control; and, as a consequence

1

- providing sufficient resources to enable the planning function to be effective — especially for the development and motivation of skilled and knowledgeable people.

These factors are entirely the responsibility of senior managers, but once this commitment has been made, then there is a great need for training and the development of knowledge and skill. The Authors hope that this guide will help in this.

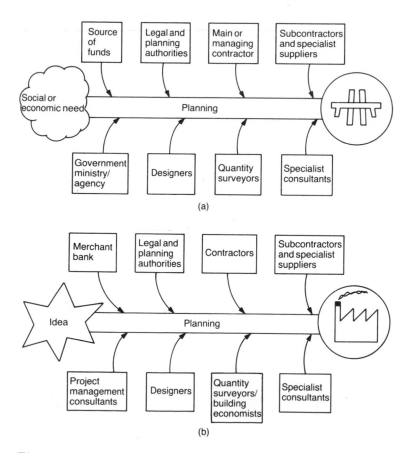

(a)

(b)

Fig. 1. Examples of people and organizations whose activities must be planned and co-ordinated during (a) public sector and (b) private sector construction projects

1.1. Planning: the common thread

The term planning can be applied to the whole of a construction project, from beginning to end, from inception and feasibility study to final commissioning and handing over the completed works to the client. It includes the planning of the design as well as the site construction work. One of the most difficult aspects of the early stage of planning is the need to co-ordinate the diversity of people and organizations that become involved, and the necessary activities and processes. Fig. 1 illustrates how planning provides the common and unifying thread; planning is one of the essential activities that must be continuous throughout the life of the project.

The project manager's power to influence the course of the project diminishes as the project progresses and this is illustrated in Fig. 2. As decisions are made, actions taken, designs made and contracts entered into, the project takes a more definite shape and opportunities to make changes disappear. It is clear that the early

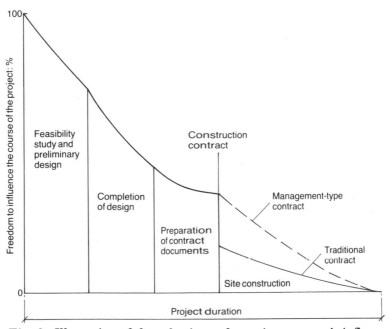

Fig. 2. Illustration of the reduction of a project manager's influence on a project as the project progresses

decisions have far reaching effects, and so must be made in a well-planned and objective way.

Further into the project, planning the construction work is an activity that will be familiar to most civil engineers, where planning lays the foundation for the control of what is usually the most expensive and fast moving phase of a construction project. The main difficulty here is keeping up to date with the inevitable and unavoidable unplanned events that occur, and replanning to achieve project objectives.

Obviously, planning whole projects is a wide and diverse subject, so this guide concentrates mainly on planning for the construction phase of a project — but within the concept of the overall common thread of construction management.

1.2. The project manager

Throughout this book it has been assumed that all projects will have project managers whose duties will include planning and the management of the planning function. This may seem to be an obvious statement to those readers whose experience is in the site construction phase of projects, where there is always a project manager — although they may use the more traditional terms agent or site manager. Traditionally, the client has appointed an engineer who has acted as the client's project manager in addition to designing the works. In recent years, it has become increasingly common for clients to take a more direct part in the management of their investments, and appoint their own project managers at the inception of a project — often using specialist project management consultants — whose task is to manage for them the entire project from inception to completion and hand over. (This strategy is often known as total project management.) Although this guide has been written principally for contractors, much of it will therefore be relevant to clients' project managers.

1.3. The objectives of planning

In general, the main objectives of planning are as follows.

• *Analysis* which is envisaging how the job will be done, in what order and with what resources; reducing the project, or part of the project, to a number of manageable activities. Each activity should be readily identifiable as a coherent piece of work, ideally relating to the project management structure and thus under the control of a specific individual.

- *Anticipation* which is to foresee potential difficulties, to plan to overcome them, and to anticipate risks so that their effects can be minimized. It can be argued that this is the major objective of construction planning, because civil engineering is a fairly high risk business, and the planning of many activities is fraught with uncertainty.

- *Scheduling resources* to enable optimum use to be made of the available and most economic resources, for each project and — taking all projects together — for the organization as a whole.

- *Co-ordination and control* to provide a basis for co-ordinating the work of the parties and contractors participating in the project, and to provide a basis for predicting and controlling time and cost.

- *Production of data* to enable planning data to be acquired for use in the preparation of future plans.

These objectives are illustrated in the case histories in chapter 7.

1.4. Planning and planning techniques

It is most important to distinguish between planning and the use of planning techniques.

- *Planning* is the creative and demanding mental activity of working out what has to be done, how, by when, by whom, and with what, i.e. doing the job in the mind. Plans are not just pieces of paper. Plans represent the results of careful thought, comprehensive discussions, decisions and actions, and commitments made between people and contractual parties.

- *Planning techniques* form the planner's tool-kit; they assist in the analysis of the plan, organizing the information, and have a crucial effect on the way in which the plan is communicated to others.

Taken together, these two elements of planning produce the plan: a strategy and tactics for the execution of the project, in terms of activities, time, quantities, resources, and perhaps costs and values. The plan is expressed as charts and reports and forms the basis

CONSTRUCTION PLANNING

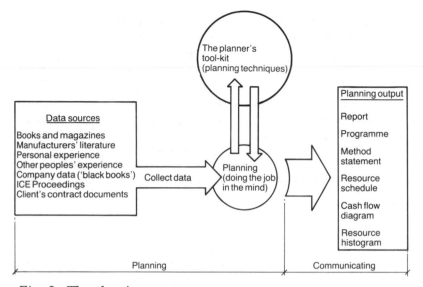

Fig. 3. The planning process

for communicating what has been planned. This process is illustated in Fig. 3.

The importance of this distinction between planning and the use of planning techniques is that it is clear that planners cannot plan without managers; without managerial involvement planners are reduced to theorists. The professional specialist planner's task is to provide the analytical skill, technical knowledge and basic data which will underpin the managerial planning process. It is the manager's task to plan; that is, to decide on strategies and tactics, to break down the work to be done into tasks and subtasks, and to assign the responsibility for completing these tasks to individuals or organizations. The programme of work is only as good as the quality of the planning. Thus again the vital role of management in planning is emphasized, a role that cannot be delegated to 'the people in Planning and their computers'.

1.5. Planning data

Planning depends on data. Without reliable and relevant data, planning can only process best guesses (although this can be better than no planning at all). Fig. 3 illustrates the way in which data are used in the planning process, and typical outputs.

6

As each construction project is different, it is difficult to make an accurate prediction on the likely duration of the design and construction activities. Therefore, all projects are a learning process for the project management, and this learning should enable more accurate predictions to be made as the project progresses. These new data can be used to refine or revise the plan. As more accurate data are acquired, it becomes possible to plan at a level of detail that would have been quite unrealistic at the start of the project.

An additional factor is the availability of data which have been assembled for purposes other than planning; for example, in a design office, monthly or weekly time sheets are used to cost engineers' time to projects, but these same time sheets may also provide useful data for planning.

1.6. Planning in the organization

Planning is part of the job of most civil engineers, but in many organizations there is a clear role for the specialist planner. This is especially true of the contractor who obtains work by competitive tendering. With a tender success rate of one in six or less, drawing up tender plans has to be cost-effective. The planning techniques described in chapter 3 can be mastered reasonably easily, but it takes familiarity and practice to use them with speed, and only specialists can develop this skill.

Fitting a specialist planner into an organization requires careful thought. If the planner's work is to have value, those who have to implement the plans must believe in them. The planner must gain the respect of those whom he or she serves; the planner's work must be realistic and credible; and the planner must be co-operative and have the ability to work well with other people. The most brilliant plans will fail if the planner has not incorporated the ideas and wishes of the project manager and the rest of the project team in the plan, but obtaining this infomation from busy people requires considerable skill and persistence. Thus personality is an important factor to be considered when appointing a planner.

Within an organization, benefits may be gained by grouping planners together to form a service department. This will result in a uniformity of approach and presentation that will make the output easier to comprehend by those who use it. Additionally, the formation of such a department will facilitate the compilation of planning data, allow better use of expensive computer installations, and enable a training programme to be more easily maintained.

The one disadvantage of creating a planning department is the risk of creating a them-and-us relationship between planners and implementers. Thus even though the planner may be based in an office remote from the work itself, every effort must be made to ensure that the planner is treated as part of the project team. Planners must make a very positive effort to keep in touch with the realities of construction project management. Senior management must provide the means for them to do it, accepting the travel and other costs as an essential part of the planning process.

1.7. The cost of planning

For any project or firm, a decision has to be made on the size and cost of the planning function. Clearly, the employment of large

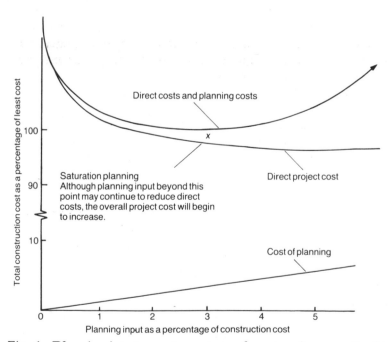

Fig. 4. Planning input as a percentage of construction cost. In this example saturation planning occurs when planning input is about 3% of total construction cost

Table 1. The cost of planning

Activity	Planning cost/total project cost: %
Petrochemical and process industry projects with frequent design changes, requiring full-time on-site planners.	2–4
Multi-disciplinary industrial projects, complex civil engineering projects.	1–2
Fully designed projects with few post-contract changes.	0·5

numbers of planners cannot in itself ensure against project over-run and overspend. There must be a point for every project when further spending on planning brings no saving in project cost, but instead merely adds to the overheads and therefore increases the total cost (Fig. 4). This saturation planning begins at the low point (*X*) of the total cost curve. Table 1 suggests a range of values for sensible spending on planning, derived from experience rather than theory. The range of figures given reflects the nature and complexity of construction projects.

To put these costs in context, a civil engineering contractor bidding keenly for a project may tender with a net profit margin of 2–4%; that is, the expected profit is of a similar size to the expected planning cost.

2 Early decisions

Decisions made early in a project often have a profound influence on the success of later activities. This is especially true of project planning. Before starting to prepare any plan, it is vital to establish who the plan is for, what level of detail is required, and its time-scale. It is essential to give careful thought to establishing this strategic framework before starting on the planning in more detail.

Planning is a difficult and time-consuming process, and early decisions on the way in which a particular plan will be made can have immense influence on the efficiency of the planning process. It is the Authors' experience that one of the skills that makes a project manager effective is the ability to set up the project properly at the beginning; certainly the Authors' experience is that projects were more successful when they had learned from experience to identify where the major problems would occur, and how to plan around them. This chapter discusses these major, early decisions.

2.1. Who is the plan for?
As in all management activities, it is essential to identify the target. Substantial construction projects can generate enormous quantities of information, and the planner must make an objective selection. Table 2 lists the people who may require or prepare a construction plan, summarizes what they will want or need to know from it, and gives appropriate time-scales.

2.2. What should be the level of detail?
When first confronted with the need to plan, it is the Authors' experience that most engineers will try to do this in great detail,

making a plan that represents reality as faithfully as possible. This would be fine if the planner could be more or less certain that the plan would work out exactly as intended, but in practice this rarely happens. Apart from a human's obvious inability to predict future events with certainty and in detail, it is obvious also that for each individual to plan in this great level of detail, at the beginning, would create the most unmanageable co-ordination problem. The quantity of information would be truly amazing, the confusion profound. In fact, it may be easier to just get on and complete the project!

Figure 5 illustrates how the level of detail may be related to the needs of the task in hand. The outer frame represents the whole plan: this would show every detail for every activity in the project, for every profession and trade. What the project manager and planner have to do is to decide on the required size and shape of the planning window for each of a number of plans which will serve different purposes. Thus Fig. 5 shows that the clients are usually more concerned about overall results than detailed methods and

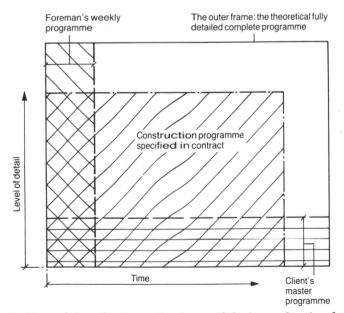

Fig. 5. Determining the size and shape of the inner planning frame or window

Table 2. *Who is the plan for?*

Clients	Plan drawn up		Primary purpose of plan	Scope of plan	Scope of programme	Time-scale	Unit	Level of detail
	For	By						
	Central government Local government Public utility	Project director	Administrative planning	A project overview from identification of need through feasibility study, preliminary design, (public inquiry), detail design, land acquisition, preparation of documents, construction period, maintenance period to adoption.	Outline project programme	Entire project	Month	Low
	Private sector industrialist or entrepreneur	Project director	Financial planning	A project overview from project conception to production and payback, including appointment of consultant/management contractor, design and documentation periods, construction, process installation, commissioning, trial production, full production.	Outline project programme	Entire project	Month	Low

Managers							
Project manager	Project manager	Co-ordination of design and construction	Design period, documentation, letting contracts, construction and maintenance periods, commissioning.	Outline and broad details	Project design and construction	Week	Low/medium
Contractor	Contractor's staff	Tender plan	All activities within construction period in sufficient detail to enable contractor to prepare the tender and particularly to price the preliminaries.	Construction programme	Construction period	Week	Medium
The Engineer		Working plan	A reassessment of the tender plan with more detail.				
		Contract plan (cl. 14)	An official version of the working plan to satisfy the conditions of contract requirements.				
Contractor Subcontractor Engineer's Representative	Contractor's staff	Resource planning	Every activity, major items of plant, dates of key material deliveries and movement of subcontractors.	Short-term programme	6–10 weeks	Day	Medium/high
Foreman Tradesman	Contractor's staff	Detailed disposition of plant and manpower	Every operation (part of activity) with the actual plant, manpower and supervisors employed.	Weekly programme	1–2 weeks	Half-day	High

require a programme to go beyond the end of the construction period, to include commissioning. In contrast, the foreman on-site will need a programme which provides some precise and detailed guidance on what he is required to do in the relatively short time-scale of one or two weeks. Other programmes will require windows of different dimensions: for example, the programme required by clause 14 of the standard form of civil engineering contract requires most of the elements of a client's master plan; but because it is principally required by the client's technical representative as an aid to managing the project on a monthly or quarterly basis, it will have less detail.

It is important not to overplan. The first consideration is what is known with any certainty, because it is futile to plan in more detail than this. The most practical approach is to acknowledge that as the project progresses, the information available to the managers and planners increases, and their experience and understanding deepens, so they can make better and more certain plans in greater detail. Thus, the level of detail, in most cases, becomes greater during the project. Original plans, made with little information to hand — especially when planning the design phase of the project — must be fairly vague in many respects; so the plan is expressed in broad terms. Gradually, through a process of learning and development, it becomes possible to make better estimates of what is required, and then planning in greater detail becomes meaningful.

This concept is called *dynamic planning*. Too often effective planning becomes inhibited by the view that 'we must work to the plan' — the original plan, of course. Certainly, there will always be a contract plan, agreed between client and contractor at the outset, but this plan can only have reflected the knowledge available to the planners at the time it was made. Furthermore, the contractual plan is usually expressed in broad terms, showing what major items of work must be complete at specific times. Within this, there is ample scope for the good project manager and planner to develop the plan as more knowledge and understanding becomes available.

Naturally a note of caution must be expressed here, because commercial factors may limit the extent to which construction contractors may, or may wish to, deviate from the contractual plan. Also, undisciplined perpetual replanning is not being advocated, but the systematic development of broad strategic plans to greater levels of detail. Of course, complete revisions are sometimes necessary when there is a substantial change of design or project management strategy, but these are major exercises and should not be undertaken without well-proven need.

The concept of dynamic planning is central to the use of computer-based planning systems. If the intention is to prepare only one plan, at the beginning, it may be easier and quicker to do it by hand. Computers are beneficial when plans are developed in more detail as the project progresses, when new well-presented output can be available immediately after each revision. Computers are almost essential for systematic monitoring, for similar reasons.

2.3. What should be the time-scale?

The time-scale is most important, and is not just a question of choosing months or weeks or days or hours, solely with regard to the necessary level of detail. The process of control and frequency of monitoring used by the firm, or specified for the project, should be the first consideration. This will be explained in more detail in chapter 5. Fig. 6 illustrates some plans and suggests appropriate time-scales, which are related to Table 2.

2.4. Planning hierarchy

In practice, plans are prepared on an hierarchical basis, with a plan at a particular level of detail being expanded to greater detail as the execution of the work becomes more imminent. It is only in this way that all plans will be consistent. Table 2 illustrates such an hierarchy of plans.

2.5. Programme duration

Obviously, programme duration is one of the most important early decisions. There are two ways to determine how long the project will take

- *it is imposed* by external considerations of the time available or allowable, and the designer or contractor then has to devise a plan to meet this requirement, or

- *it is built up* from a detailed analysis of the work to be done and the resources available, using estimates of the time required for each specific activity.

15

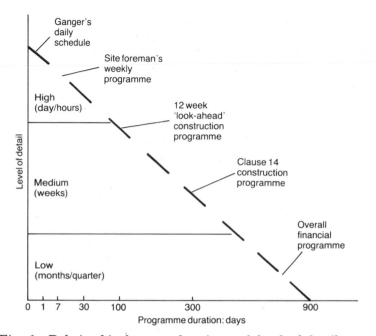

Fig. 6. Relationship between duration and level of detail; e.g. a programme for a foreman may be one day in duration but require every hour in the day to be accounted for, whereas a programme for a financier may cover three years but require an assessment every three months

Examples 1–3 are examples of externally imposed considerations. Examples 4 and 5 are examples of durations built up from a detailed analysis of the work to be done and the resources which are available.

Example 1: Earthmoving weather window
In many regions of the UK it is unwise to attempt bulk earthmoving using scrapers between October and March. If, for example, it is required to move 400 000 m³ of earth starting on 1 August, the weather constraint dictates that this must be completed in two months. So with scrapers capable of moving, on average, 20 000 m³ per month each, 10 scrapers will be required. This is a large number of scrapers, and special measures may have to be taken to allow them to work effectively on anything but a large site.

Example 2: Summer paving window
In the UK, concrete highway paving with contraction joints is only permitted between 21 April and 21 October.

Example 3: Client's constraints
The client may often

- have an economic need for fast construction; for example, the level of turnover and profit from a large retail store usually justifies quite considerable expenditure on methods to achieve rapid construction.

- require a project to be constructed in stages, for economic or practical reasons; for example, to spread the cost of a large development over a longer period, and to generate income from the completed stages to help finance the remaining work; or to rebuild an existing sewage treatment works while keeping it in operation.

- require work to be done during a factory holiday shutdown.

Example 4: Duration determined by the output of a major resource
It is often the case that the output of a construction operation, or a complete project, is determined by the output of a key item of plant; this is most common in dredging, pile driving and road building.

Example 5: Duration determined to achieve minimum cost
In many cases, contractors use recorded data on the method and output of similar operations completed in the past to assess the combination of resources most likely to complete the work at minimum direct cost. The duration of the operation is then calculated from the volume of work to be done in this way.

2.6. Activity and activity duration
Although what follows is not part of the early decision-making process described earlier in this chapter, the reader should not proceed to chapter 3 without a clear understanding of what is meant by *activity* and *activity duration*.

The four planning techniques described in chapter 3 all require projects to be analysed and broken down into convenient work units or activities. The scope or work content of each activity is, of itself, not important. What is important is that the planner must be able, with the planned resources, to decide how long it will take to complete. For example, an activity for a bridge project might be

- Construct pier foundation: duration 10 days.

An equally valid activity might be less encompassing:

- Fix formwork to pier foundation: duration 2 days.

Providing that the planner understands the meaning of the activity within the project and can determine a duration for the activity, it may be as large and embracing, or as small and detailed, as the planner wishes.

2.7. Activity duration

As part of a large stormwater drainage project, consider an activity for constructing a water storage lagoon by excavating 1800 m³ of firm clay and depositing it around the excavation to form a bund. Table 3 gives four construction methods for carrying out this activity with durations varying from one to 50 days. As every method is valid, which one should the planner select?

When faced with such a decision the first rule to follow is

- Choose an activity duration based on the most economical and appropriate use of resources.

If the storage lagoon is located in a country where unskilled labour is abundant and inexpensive, methods 1 or 2 will be economic and appropriate. The choice between the extremes of five and 50 days will depend on the urgency of the project as a whole. If the storage lagoon is in a country where labour is scarce and more expensive it would be constructed by a method somewhere between methods 3 and 4. In this case the plant used would be considered in relation to the other plant likely to be on site. The large excavator called for in method 4 would only be used if such a machine was already available on site or the need to save time exceeded the need for economic operation.

From this example it may be appreciated that individual activity durations must also be related to the time available for the project as a whole. Table 4 suggests a logical sequence of examining a project to establish a general understanding of the urgency of the pro-

18

Table 3. Example of estimating an activity duration, illustrating the first rule

Activity: Excavate a storage lagoon 30 m × 30 m × 2 m in firm clay and deposit spoil in perimeter bunds; total volume 1800 m³

Method	Resources employed	Output	Activity duration: days
1	18 labourers with hand tools	2 m³ per man-day	50
2	180 labourers with hand tools	2 m³ per man-day	5
3	360° excavator (0·2 m³ bucket) 2 dumpers (0·5 m³) 1 roller 4 operatives 1 banksman	240 m³ per 8 h day	7·5
4	360° excavator (1·5 m³ bucket) 3 tippers (6·0 m³) 2 rollers 6 operatives 2 banksmen	1800 m³ per 8 h day	1

ject and the time available for groups of activities. The second rule for determining activity durations is therefore

● Ensure the activity duration relates to the time available for the entire project.

Returning to Table 3 it can be seen that the activity durations were arrived at by assembling a group of resources (gang) and then deciding an output for that gang. This task, more than any other planning task, requires a detailed knowledge of construction resources and an understanding developed from personal site experience. As such a personal database takes many years to develop, it is not surprising that having acquired this knowledge, planners jealously guard it in private and personal 'black books'. Fortunately, there are alternatives to a personal black book in the Builders and Estimators Price Books which are published

Table 4. Estimating duration

1. Identify constraints imposed by the client, e.g. overall project duration, availability of site, stages of construction.
2. List constraints imposed by third parties, e.g. timing of road and services diversions, limited hours for noisy operations, access for heavy vehicles.
3. Note the weather windows.
4. Note the public and industry holidays.
5. Decide on the method of construction: this will provide the broad strategy, the major items of equipment and other resources.
6. Determine the durations of the principal operations.
7. Fit in the remaining operations to achieve the best use of resources.
The first five steps will usually have divided the project into a number of sections. This will enable these sections to be planned in detail more realistically.

annually.[1-3] Other sources of resources output information are given in references 4–7. Table 4 can be used as a check-list or as the basis for a graphical method of duration examination using the planning techniques described in chapter 3.

There is one further point to make about the determination of activity durations, namely to use output rates that reflect *average* performance and allow for all the non-productive operations, human fallibility and the constraints of weather and workplace; e.g.

- for plant items: refuelling, maintenance, breakdowns

- for humans: sickness, tiredness

- weather: rain, low temperatures

- workplace: tidal work, confined spaces, hazardous sites.

2.8. Summary
Early decisions

Before starting to prepare a plan, consider the following questions

- who is the plan for?

- what should be the level of detail?

- what should be the time-scale?

Project duration

Can the project duration be decided on by the planner or will it be imposed by external considerations?

Activities

When fixing activity durations use the most economic and appropriate resources, ensure they relate to the time available for the entire project and use average output rates.

3 Planning techniques

Four techniques are used commonly in construction planning: bar charts, network analysis, line-of-balance and linear programmes. This chapter explains how these techniques are used, and gives guidance on selecting the right technique for the job in hand.

Chapters 1 and 2 have laid the foundations for construction planning. The next two chapters describe the techniques used by the professional planner. This is the planner's tool-kit. As with all tools they must be used intelligently, and sometimes adapted to overcome a specific and unusual problem. The Authors' experience is that good planners are inventive people, and they can create custom-built techniques to suit specific problems and circumstances. This is as it should be, and it is not the intention that the techniques described in this guide should be applied rigidly, in exactly the way described. The reality is that there is a whole family of techniques, and variations of techniques. Obviously some logical rules have to be observed, and consistency of application and presentation is essential, but within these requirements there is much flexibility.

3.1. The anatomy of planning techniques

Before describing planning techniques in detail, it is useful to look at the components that form the tools in the planner's tool-kit. Most planning techniques aim to express the work to be done, to a time-scale; some also include resources, and perhaps cost and value. In simple terms, they aim to help control time and cost. The other major factor in project control, quality, is controlled by its own family of control techniques; and quality is related to time and cost through the skill and judgement of the project management team. The major components of planning techniques are

- activities: literally, being busy, expending energy, consuming resources, taking time; in construction planning, this means a job to be done; for example preparing a drawing, an order to be placed, a hole to be dug, bricks to be laid in a wall, a flow of water to be diverted.

- activity durations: the time required for the completion of each activity.

- project time-scale: the time structure of the project; it is usual to give each week in the project a number (this makes calculation easier), and these then have to be related to calendar dates, holidays, etc.

- event: an occurrence at a specific point in time; for example, the granting of planning consent, or the start or end of a traffic diversion.

- work method: the plan must be expressed in some logical way, indicating the sequence of operations, and which activities and events are interrelated; this may be implicit (as with bar charts) or explicit (in network analysis, where work method is usually called logic).

- resources: often called the four Ms (men, machines, materials, and money) but can also include overheads (for example, site accommodation), and even such essentials as managerial skill.

- costs: what the work has or will cost, often derived directly from the unit costs of the individual resources.

- value: what has or can be earned by payment for work done derived from the bill of quantities, the estimate or an internal budget. The calculation of value-to-date can be used as an overall measure of project progress.

3.2. The planner's tool-kit

The main tools are the bar chart, the line-of-balance, the linear programme and network analysis. There are other tools, such as physical models in two and three dimensions, and computer models.

The bar chart

The bar chart is everybody's favourite. It is easy to draw, easy to understand, and not too searching of managerial skill; it is best used for straightforward, well-understood construction work, with simple relationships between the activities. This graphical technique still forms the basis for most resource scheduling. One of its main disadvantages is that changes in plan require extensive redrafting.

Line-of-balance

Line-of-balance is a specialized technique for repetitive work. It was derived from manufacturing industry, and has been found to be effective in planning work that is truly repetitive. Examples of successful applications include planning the construction of identical floors in high rise construction, and large housing developments. The first case study in chapter 7 is a low-cost housing scheme in a developing country, for which the construction of a large development of identical houses was planned using line-of-balance.

Line-of-balance has been found to be difficult to use on projects which require a large number of trades or operations to construct each identical unit. The problems arise not from the technique itself, but from the difficulty of showing all the information on one chart, especially when using the technique to monitor progress. When used to plan, it can be an excellent means of relating resources, activity durations and the general pace of work on site.

Linear programme (or time-chainage chart)

Linear programming is a specialized technique for linear work. This is a basic tool of UK road contractors, and the second case study in chapter 7 shows the use of this technique to maximum effect. Other successful applications include the construction of a large canal in a developing country, and it is especially useful in tunnelling.

Like line-of-balance, this is a simple two-dimensional graphical technique and can show clearly only a limited amount of information and a limited degree of complexity.

Network analysis

Network analysis is a powerful, logical and analytical technique. It is most effective when used for complicated projects, especially those with external constraints and complex interrelationships.

The technique is based on drawing the logical relationships between construction operations, and — from an analysis of the relative durations — establishing which operations have the most crucial effect on the project duration. It can be drawn in a number of ways, the most well-known in the UK being the arrow diagram. The technique is sometimes known as the critical path method (CPM), and critical path analysis (CPA). A version which incorporates a statistical method for calculating the probability that a project will be completed on a specific date is called the programme evaluation and review technique (PERT).

Network analysis has a good and comprehensive logical basis, lends itself easily to computer processing, and can be used as an effective control tool. These excellent characteristics are also its principal weakness, because it is easy for the planner to be drawn into a level of planning and analysis that is much too detailed and advanced for most construction projects.

3.3. Which technique?

Like any other professional, the planner has to select the right tool for the job. An engineer does not use a theodolite to take levels! He could of course, but he would be using a tool that was unnecessarily sophisticated for the task in hand. Similarly, a planner does not use network analysis for a simple job. Similar analogies can be drawn between the more specialized survey instruments (such as vertical plumbing devices) and linear programmes and line-of-balance; these do a special but limited job very well.

Figure 7 is a planning technique selection chart. It will be noted that sometimes the client requires the use of network analysis, often for good reasons of his own, in which case the contractor's choice is more limited. Nevertheless, specialized techniques may still be used where required, and integrated into a master network programme in the ways described in section 3.7.

It is of fundamental importance to note that the *level of detail* of the plan and the *choice of technique* are related. For example, the overall programme for a large and complex industrial project should be drawn as a network (as indicated in Fig. 7). Suppose that one activity on that programme is 'construct road'; obviously this is fine at this level of detail, but what technique should be used by the engineer who has to plan the construction of this road

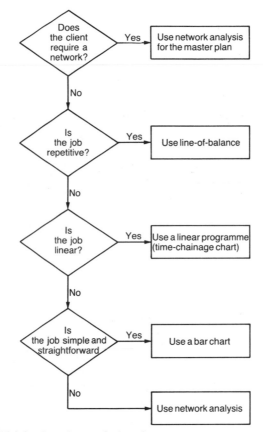

Fig. 7. Which planning technique?

in more detail? Of course, a linear programme should be used. Failure to recognize this vital principle has caused great problems in the past; for example, where firms have adopted a policy of using network analysis for everything, only to find that it does not work too well for the construction of a road — and the engineer in charge of the road then concludes that network analysis does not work! For this reason, Fig. 7 asks questions about the job, not the project; the job is the work to be planned, at a specific level of detail.

Table 5 summarizes the characteristics of the techniques, and the basic principles of the techniques will be described in the following sections.

Table 5. The planner's tool-kit

Technique	Planning uses	Programme uses	Progress control use
Bar chart	Simple projects	Good communicating tool Universally understood In common use Good basis for resource scheduling Most computer systems give bar chart from network	Absense of explicit logic relationships limits usefulness Tedious to update manually
Line-of-balance	Repetitive work (houses, precast concrete production, multi-storey buildings)	Good communicating tool Demonstrates trade interference	Useful planning tool Difficult to show a lot of detail clearly Illustrates general pace of work and trade intereference
Linear programme	Linear products (highways, tunnels railways, viaducts)	Good communicating tool Demonstrates interrelationship of sequential operations	Useful planning tool Progress shown easily if plan kept simple
Network analysis	Complex projects Management contracts Design management	Poor communicating tool in network form Usually converted to bar chart for general use	Powerful control tool especially for large numbers of contractors Forms basis of most computer systems

3.4. Bar charts

Basic bar chart

As a means of planning, programming and communicating, the bar chart is hard to beat. It is simple in concept, easy to construct and equally easy to understand; it is hardly surprising therefore that it is the most widely used technique in the planners' tool-kit.

Figure 8 shows part of a bar chart for a factory extension. The activities are listed down the left hand side, the time-scale is drawn horizontally and the bars represent the time when work will proceed on the activities. It is usual, although not essential, to list activities in their planned chronological order of performance; this gives a diagonal pattern of time bars across the chart which provides an added visual stimulus to the representation of progress.

The basic bar chart is an excellent means of relating activities to time; however, as a planning technique, it has a number of shortcomings

- it does not show relationships between activities

- it does not indicate the rate of progress within each time bar

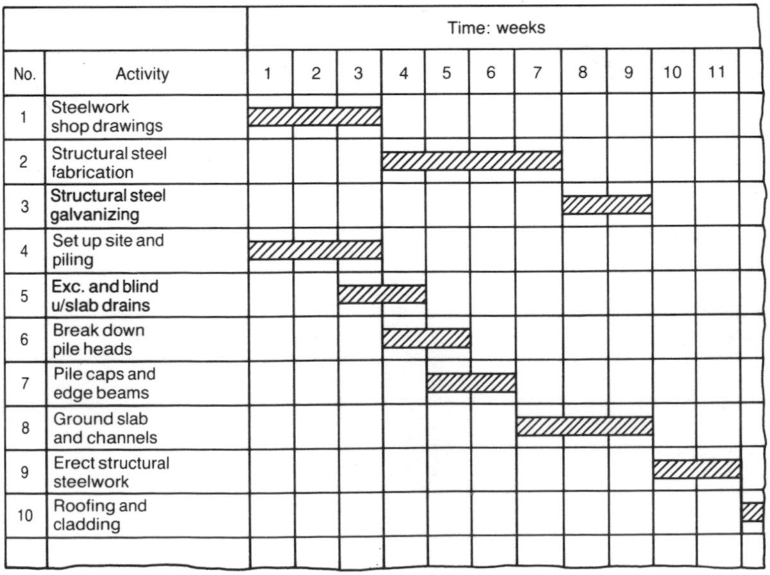

No.	Activity	1	2	3	4	5	6	7	8	9	10	11
						Time: weeks						
1	Steelwork shop drawings	▨	▨	▨								
2	Structural steel fabrication					▨	▨	▨	▨			
3	Structural steel galvanizing									▨	▨	
4	Set up site and piling	▨	▨	▨								
5	Exc. and blind u/slab drains				▨	▨						
6	Break down pile heads					▨	▨					
7	Pile caps and edge beams						▨	▨				
8	Ground slab and channels								▨	▨		
9	Erect structural steelwork										▨	▨
10	Roofing and cladding											▨

Fig. 8. Basic chart for a factory extension

- it does not relate activities to location.

To overcome these shortcomings several variations to the basic bar chart have been developed. They are the linked bar chart; the monitoring bar chart; and the subdivided bar chart.

Linked bar chart

Figure 9 shows a bar chart where the planner has linked the horizontal time bars with vertical lines (links) to indicate the construction logic. For example, the link between activities 9 and 10 is in effect a statement that 'the roofing and cladding cannot begin until the steelwork erection is complete'. This is so obvious that the link is almost redundant, but the logic connection between activities 3 and 9 may not be quite so obvious and without that link the site manager might have thought he was free to start activity 9 earlier by overlapping it with the preceding activity.

The addition of links makes the bar chart a more practical technique for site use, particularly when it becomes necessary to revise the programme. A delay in activity 2 of one week due to late production of shop drawings will also delay activities 3, 9 and 10 by

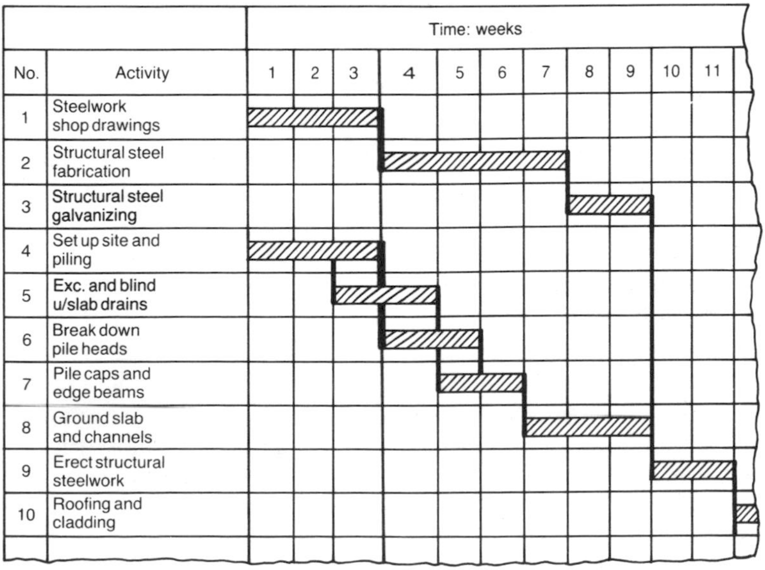

No.	Activity	Time: weeks										
		1	2	3	4	5	6	7	8	9	10	11
1	Steelwork shop drawings	▨	▨									
2	Structural steel fabrication				▨	▨	▨					
3	Structural steel galvanizing								▨			
4	Set up site and piling	▨	▨									
5	Exc. and blind u/slab drains				▨							
6	Break down pile heads				▨							
7	Pile caps and edge beams					▨						
8	Ground slab and channels							▨				
9	Erect structural steelwork										▨	
10	Roofing and cladding											▨

Fig. 9. Linked bar chart for a factory extension

29

one week and extend the overall project time. Without the links the significance of the delay to activity 9 might not have been so obvious. The addition of links to express construction logic works well when the time bars can be plotted diagonally across the diagram and when the project is straightforward. As shown in Fig. 7, for complex projects it is generally better to use network analysis, but bar charts can then be drawn from the network for communication purposes.

A further enhancement is the cascade. By means of a mathematical sorting technique, activities can be printed as chains of bars with similar values of float, those with least float being printed at the top of the chart (float will be defined in section 3.7.) This gives the characteristic cascade appearance, as sequentially linked bars progress across and down the chart, as in a cascade of water. The clever trick is to avoid depending links crossing over excessively, which would make the diagram very difficult to interpret. This is a tedious process to analyse by hand, and cascade charts are usually done by computer systems. The advantage, of course, is that the ordering of a bar chart into activities of progressively less criticality, focuses managements' minds on the vitally important issues.

Monitoring bar chart

In addition to indicating an intended programme for the project, bar charts can be used to monitor progress by showing a second bar drawn for the actual dates worked. For accurate monitoring, this second bar is only of limited help, because it shows only when work was proceeding on the activity. Looking at Fig. 10, one may only deduce that the activity has started; it is impossible to see how much has been done or whether progress on the activity is behind or ahead of schedule. By the addition of expected and actual percentage completions, as shown in Fig. 11, a more accurate estimate of progress may be made. Chapter 5 deals in more detail with the mechanics of the monitoring progress; the purpose of introducing monitoring at this stage is to acquaint the reader with the format of the chart.

Subdivided bar chart

There are certain types of projects, particularly those where the work is spread out, where the planner might find it useful to relate

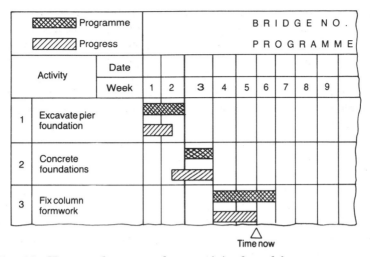

Fig. 10. How much progress has activity 3 made?

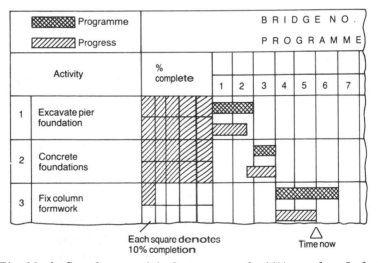

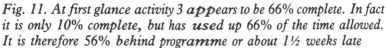

Fig. 11. At first glance activity 3 appears to be 66% complete. In fact it is only 10% complete, but has used up 66% of the time allowed. It is therefore 56% behind programme or about 1½ weeks late

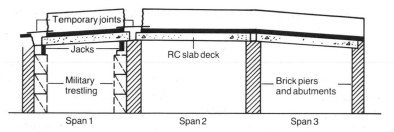

Fig. 12. *Cross-section of road over rail bridge showing temporary works for jacking superstructure*

the time bars to the location of the work. One way of doing this is to subdivide the activity list into sections as in Figs 12 and 13. This works quite well for this bridge reconstruction where the piers divide the structure into obvious sections.

Management structure is another basis for subdivision. If the activities are grouped into sections which correspond to the division of responsibility on the project, the person in charge of each

	Activity	Week	1	2	3	
Span 1	Excavate road at bearings Make temporary joints		▨			
	Erect military trestling for jack platforms		▨	▨		
	Jack span and renew bearings		*Road closure ▨			
Span 2	Reposition trestling			▨	▨	
	Excavate road at bearings Make temporary joints			▨		
	Jack span and renew bearings			*Road closure ▨		

Fig. 13. Bar chart for superstructure work; activities are subdivided according to spans

32

section can obtain most of the information required from just one section of the chart.

Good practice

Even though bar charts are simple, they will be more useful if planned and drawn with care. The draughting process can be made easier by providing good standard bar chart blanks with faint guidelines for planning and monitoring bars. Each organization will have its own special requirements for standard sheets, but generally for detailed project planning the sizes shown in Table 6 should be suitable.

It is common practice to leave a space at the bottom of the chart which can be used for resource aggregation (chapter 4) or monitoring (chapter 5). Fig. 14 shows a useful multi-purpose layout for a bar chart suitable for these purposes.

3.5. Line-of-balance
Basic principles

Line-of-balance is used to plan the construction of a number of similar items. The technique is used to analyse the application of labour and plant resources to ensure that each resource can progress from one item to the next in an orderly way, completing its own work on all the items without being delayed waiting for preceding work to be completed. Thus the technique aims to keep all the resources in balance, each following the other productively and having a clear run of work.

The basic principles of the technique will be described using as an example the construction of ten similar, simple houses. The house is shown in Fig. 15. The more practical and detailed aspects of line-of-balance are explained in the first case study in chapter 7, which is taken from a real project.

Table 6. Standard bar chart sheet sizes

Sheet size	Number of activities	Divisions	Purpose
A1 extended	60–80	104 weeks	Construction programme
A1	60–80	52 weeks	Construction programme
A3	30	13 weeks	Detailed look ahead
A4	10	14 days	Weekly programme

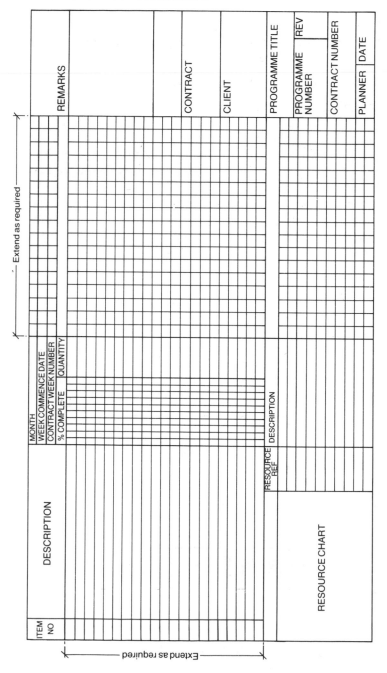

Fig. 14. A useful multi-purpose bar chart layout

Activities

Figure 16 shows a simplified **plan** for the construction of one house. The activities are

- construction of foundations (**activity** 1)

- construction of **walls** (activity 2)

- construction of roof (activity 3)

- provision of services, stage 1; usually called first fix (activity 4)

- application of **wall**, floor and ceiling finishes (activity 5)

- completion of services: second fix (activity 6)

- external works: drainage, fencing, etc. (activity 7).

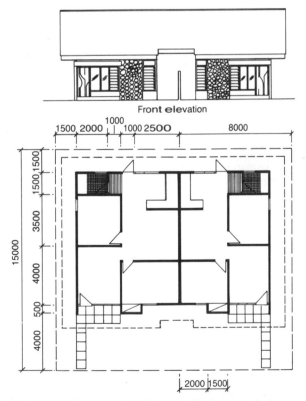

Fig. 15. House used to explain line-of-balance technique

35

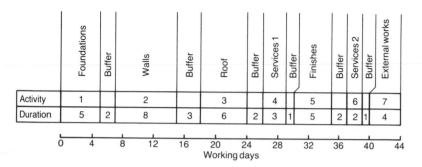

	Foundations	Buffer	Walls	Buffer	Roof	Buffer	Services 1	Buffer	Finishes	Buffer	Services 2	Buffer	External works
Activity	1		2		3		4		5		6		7
Duration	5	2	8	3	6	2	3	1	5	2	2	1	4

0   4   8   12   16   20   24   28   32   36   40   44
Working days

Fig. 16. Plan of work for one house

These activities coincide with the division of the work between the building trades. The main objective of using line-of-balance is to make optimum use of resources. To facilitate this it is important that the activities and resources are related closely; i.e. the job is planned on a trade basis.

Activity durations

The activity durations are estimated from an analysis of the work to be done, and are shown in Fig. 16, expressed in working days.

Project time-scale

Section 2.5 explains that project duration may be either imposed by external considerations, or built up from a detailed analysis of the work to be done and the resources available; or by a combination of these considerations. In this example, the initial plan will be prepared on the basis of making best use of resources. In the first case study, the use of resources is important but also the project must be completed quickly.

Work method — the plan

In construction work, estimates of activity duration cannot be anything other than approximate. In repetitive construction where the activities and trades follow in sequence, any delay in the planned completion of an activity will result in following trades waiting unproductively for its completion. Therefore it is prudent to make some provision for late completion by planning a short delay or buffer between each activity. The estimate of buffer times is related

to the project manager's assessment of the reliability of the estimate
of activity duration; where the reliability poor, large buffers must
be used.

The plan for this example project assumes that only one trade
will be working on a house at any time, so the work plan given
in Fig. 16 shows a simple linear sequence. In practice, this strategy
may result in the planned project duration being too long, and there
may be a need for several trades to work on a house simultaneously;
this more complex application of line-of-balance is illustrated in
the first case study.

The obvious choice of resources will be to employ just one gang
of each trade, so each gang will work on every house. Fig. 17 shows
this progression for activity 1, followed by activity 2, and then
by activity 3: this illustrates the problem that the line-of-balance
technique is designed to solve. Activity 2 will proceed at a slower
pace than activity 1, and this in turn will halt work on activity
3, because the roofers will be ready to start work on the third house
before the walls are finished. This problem is called interference
and is fundamental to scheduling repetitive work. Of course, in
practice the interference problem may not manifest itself in this
way; if tradesmen cannot see work available for them for some
reasonable period ahead, they may simply work more slowly —
and so cause even more problems later on in the project. This is
one reason why projects become more difficult to manage as they
progress, and is why careful planning and control will be
beneficial.

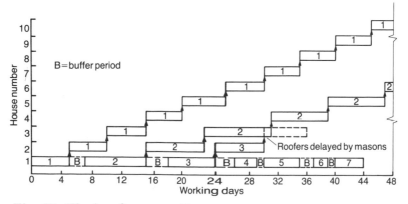

Fig. 17. The interference problem

Line-of-balance analysis

The purpose of this analysis is to balance the rate of progress of the activities, and to schedule the activities to eliminate interference. This is done by

- adjusting the rate of production for each activity, so that this approximates to a common rate of production for all activities

- delaying the start of those activities that (even after adjustment) proceed faster than the activity immediately preceding it, to maintain *at least the minimum buffer* specified at all times.

In the classical, factory-based, line-of-balance analysis, it is assumed that individual resources make equal contributions to progress, regardless of the number of the resources used. For example, if a task requires 20 man-hours, then one person would complete it in 20 hours, whereas 20 people would complete the task in one hour. Thus the rate of progress of each activity may be adjusted quite finely; consequently, the activities may be made to work at almost the same rate of progress.

In construction, such an approach is unrealistic. Tradesmen rarely work as individuals or in large groups. Years of experience and practice have established the most effective size for a group. For example, to obtain the most efficient productivity, bricklayers usually work in a team of two bricklayers serviced by one labourer. Therefore, the balancing calculations have to be done on the basis of the output of gangs, rather than individuals. This restriction makes it more difficult to achieve a common rate of work within a plan.

The second part of the analysis (maintaining the minimum buffer time by delaying the start of relevant activities) will be illustrated by using the unadjusted plan shown in Fig. 17. Plotting the schedule in the way shown in Fig. 17 is tedious; an easier method is shown in Fig. 18. The calculations are given in Table 7. To obtain the slope of the line, it is necessary to calculate T, the time required from the start of work on the first house to the start of work on the last. This value is the rate of production for this activity.

To plot the subsequent activity, it is necessary to compare the rate of production of the activity with that of the immediately preceding activity; for example, the production rate of activity 2 (72 days) is slower than the production rate of activity 1 (45 days),

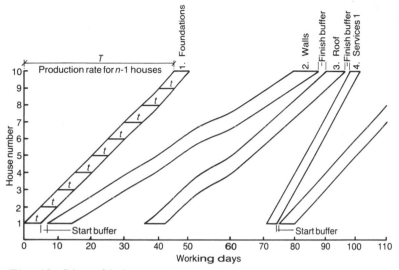

Fig. 18. Line-of-balance schedule

so activity 2 may start immediately after the buffer, without fear of interference with 1. Thus the buffer is a start buffer. Therefore the calculations for activity 2 are

start day of house 1	=	start day of activity 1 on house 1	+	duration of activity 1 for one house	+	buffer following activity 1
	=	0	+	5	+	2
	=	day 7				

start day of house 10	=	start day of activity 2 on house 1	+	T for activity 2	
	=	7	+	72	
	=	day 79			

The next activity (number 3, roof) is expected to proceed faster than activity 2. Unless the start of this work is delayed, the roofers will catch up with the masons building the walls. In this case it is the *completion* of the activity that is important, and the diagram must be drawn so that the minimum buffer is maintained between the completion of the walls on the last house and the start of the roof on that house. In this case, the buffer is an end buffer, and

39

Table 7. Calculations for line-of-balance schedule

Activity	Duration t: days	Time for $n-1$ houses T: days	Buffer: days	Type of buffer	Start day house 1	Start day house 10
1. Foundations	5	45	2	Start	0 (project start)	$0+45=45$
2. Walls	8	72	3	End	$0+5+2=7$	$7+72=79$
3. Roof	6	54	2	End	$90-54=36$	$79+8+3=90$
4. Services 1	3	27	1	Start	$98-27=71$	$90+6+2=98$
5. Finishes	5	45	2	Start	$71+3+1=75$	$75+45=120$
6. Services 2	2	18	2	End	$127-18=109$	$120+5+2=127$
7. External works	4	36	1	Start	$109+2+1=112$	$112+36=148$

Total project time $= 148 + 4 = 152$ days; approximately 30 weeks for a 5 day week.

the start of the activity on the first house is calculated backwards from the predetermined finish date. The calculations for activity 3 are

start day of house 10	=	start day of activity 2 on house 10	+	duration of activity 2 for one house	+	buffer following activity 2
	=	79	+	8	+	3
	=	day 90				

start day of house 1	=	start day of activity 3 on house 10	−	T for activity 3
	=	90	−	54
	=	day 36		

In this way, the schedule can be completed, as shown in Fig. 19. Obviously, this schedule lacks a common rate of production, so some improvement would be desirable. Fig. 20 shows that increasing the rate of production of activity 2 (walls) would enable activity 3 (roof) to start earlier. On the other hand, increasing the rate of production of activity 4 must delay the start of activity 5 relative to activity 3. The first case study shows how these adjustments may be made, giving detailed calculations.

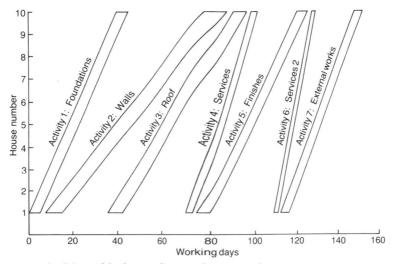

Fig. 19. Line-of-balance for ten–house project

Variations

As in all techniques, line-of-balance can be developed and varied to suit specific circumstances. Some variations are outlined in the following sections.

Parallel scheduling

The plan does not have to be a linear sequence; some activities can proceed in parallel. This is illustrated in the first case study. There may be a loss of clarity in the diagram, because the activity lines have to be superimposed on each other.

Planned hand-over schedule

In housing developments, houses are often occupied as they are completed. Thus, the project plan may be based on a planned hand-over schedule, for example, six houses per week. Such a requirement may determine the common work rate, and cause the diagram to be constructed backwards from the hand-over schedule line. The planned hand-over rate defines the approximate value of T for all activities.

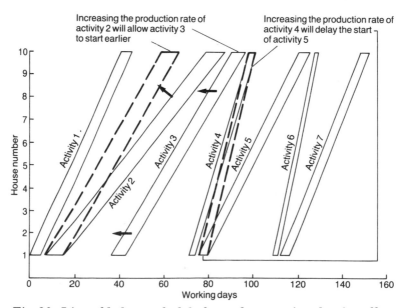

Fig. 20. Line-of-balance schedule for ten-house project showing effects of increased rate of production on activities 2 and 4

Intermittent working

Some improvement in schedules may be made by the planned use of activities that stop when interference would be imminent, and start again after a delay. For example, in Fig. 21, a services subcontractor could start activity 6 earlier than shown, complete the work on some houses, leave the site, and return at a later date to complete the work. Activity 7 (external works) can then be brought forward.

Use of spreadsheet computer programs

The balancing calculations for line-of-balance are tedious, and are an obvious application for a spreadsheet computer program. The use of these programs facilitates experimentation with alternative strategies, so encouraging the development of better plans. This is described in more detail in reference 8. The calculations for Tables 20 and 21 were done by spreadsheet, although for explanatory purposes Table 21 is shown as a hand-calculation (see section 7.1).

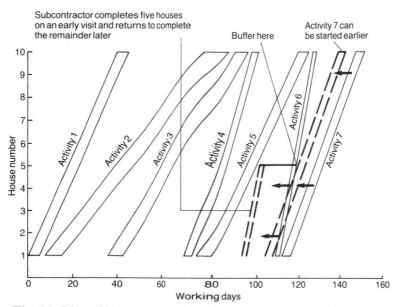

Fig. 21. *Line-of-balance schedule for ten-house project with intermittent working*

3.6. Linear programmes (time-chainage charts)

Basic principles

Linear programmes are an ideal technique for roads, railways and other projects measured by chainage; the linear programme is drawn on a large sheet of squared paper marked with the x-axis representing chainage and the y-axis the passage of time. In essence, the technique is to plot all activities showing planned progress against time and location.

In Fig. 22, the inclined line represents an activity AB which is planned to start at chainage 500 at the start of week two and to end at chainage 1500 at the end of week three. It can be seen that

- the rate of progress of the activity is represented by the slope of the inclined line. For activity AB the rate is 500 m/week

- the expected position of the gang carrying out the activity can be found at any given time by reading off the chainage against the time scale.

Activities: compact, extended, extensive and static

To represent the project activities realistically, it is best to classify them into four types; these are illustrated in Fig. 23. Representing an activity as a single line works well for a *compact activity*, i.e. one that, for any given time, occupies only a short length of the project, e.g. kerb-laying (Fig. 23(*a*)).

An *extended activity* (Fig. 23(*b*)) is used where the operation may spread over a considerable distance. It may need to be drawn as two parallel lines, each representing the start and completion of

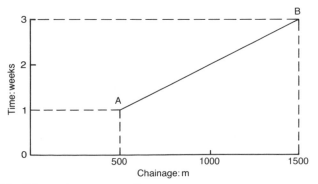

Fig. 22. Linear programme format

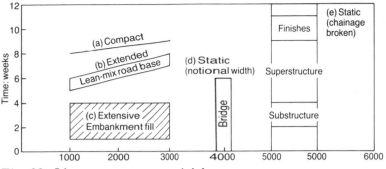

Fig. 23. Linear programme activities

the activity. The example shown in Fig. 23(*b*) is the laying of lean mix concrete road base, where the operation extends from the placing of side forms up to the point where the concrete has cured for seven days, perhaps a distance of 2 km along the road.

An *extensive activity* is one where the work occupies the entire chainage for the activity throughout its duration. For example the construction of a 1000 m-long earth embankment from a borrow pit occupies the whole of the section until the last grading of the formation. An extensive activity of this type is represented by a block (Fig. 23(*c*)).

In addition to these three continuous activities that progress along the project, there is a *static activity* which takes place once only at a certain chainage, e.g. a highway bridge or a tunnel shaft. This type of activity (which will probably also need a detailed programme all to itself) may be depicted on the linear programme by a vertical bar of notional width (Fig. 23(*d*)). If that bar needs to be widened to provide more space for the description (Fig. 23(*e*)) the chainage may be stopped on the left of the bar and restarted on the right.

Table 8. Linear programme activities

Activity	Form	Example
Compact	Inclined line	Kerb laying, fencing
Extended	Parallel inclined lines	Concrete paving
Extensive	Block	Earthworks, delays
Static	Vertical column	Bridge, junction, roundabout, tunnel shaft

Table 8 summarizes these four activity types. In practice they are not rigidly defined and it may be necessary to generate other shapes and configurations to represent specific construction methods.

With a linear programme it is easy to show constraints as non-activities. For example, because of delays in completing land purchases, a contract is let in which possession of the whole site cannot be given to the contractor at the start of the contract period. The

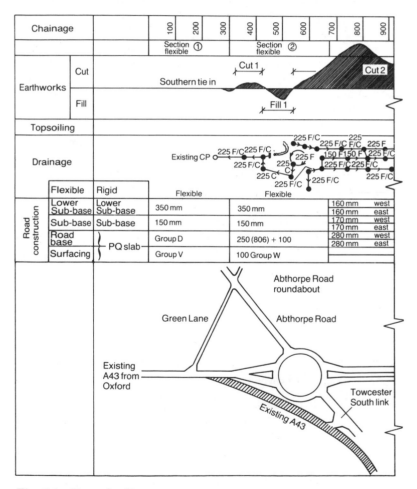

Fig. 24. Data for linear programme

extent, in both place and time, of this area of enforced non-activity may be marked on the plan in the same block form as the extensive activity.

Assembling the data

Before beginning to plot activities, all the data that may be needed should be collected together and transferred on to the chart. If the x-axis on the chart is drawn about one third up from the bottom of the sheet, a space is made available to plot data abstracted from the drawings. Fig. 24 shows how this may be done for a road project. If this step is neglected, concentration will be continually broken by the frequent need to refer to drawings and documents.

The plotting of activities will call for answers to many questions; for example

- where do kerbs start and finish?

- where are the lay-bys?

- where does the capping layer end?

- where is the sub-base thickened to 450 mm?

To ensure that the answers are no further away than the bottom of the planning sheet, it is suggested that

- a continuous simplified sketch plan of the project is drawn at the bottom of the sheet

- working up the page, the data for every individual operation are entered in the order of construction, e.g. for a road: site clearance, fencing, culverts, earthworks (first stage), drainage, formation, sub-base, paving layers, earthworks (second stage), road lines

- the start and finish is shown for every operation and any points of change, i.e. thickening of road base or change of fence type

- all the above data are marked along horizontal lines or given a more graphical treatment if this makes it clearer. Earthworks stand out particularly well when drawn as a long section.

Identify constraints

When all the data have been abstracted from the drawings and marshalled tidily below the x-axis, the next stage is to identify and

47

plot the constraints. These have already been briefly discussed in section 2.5. Constraints are imposed by

- the client
- a third party
- nature.

The check-list in Table 9 contains some common constraints. Those that are relevant must be marked on the diagram so that their effects may be allowed for in drawing up the plan.

Planning

With the abstracted project data drawn in diagrammatically at the bottom of the sheet and the constraints marked in on the time-chainage diagram, planning may begin. It will be possible to concentrate on constructing the project on paper without constantly breaking the chain of thought to refer to documents.

As planning is a creative activity and no two projects are the same, it is impossible to give any firm rules on procedure. However, the following suggestions may help.

- Generally plot activities following the same order as the construction procedure, i.e. foundations first, finishes last.

- Mark in major activities which must be carried out within weather windows.

- After marking up the sheet with major items, section completion dates and other key constraints, the project will have been divided up into a number of sections. Within each section decide on method of construction and the major items of plant to be used — this will set progress rates.

- Activities may now be fitted in on a trial-and-error basis using these progress rates. Where activities take too long to complete, resources will have to be increased to reduce times. When gaps appear in the sequence, the planner should consider shortening the programme, reducing resources or trying a later start.

Figure 25 shows part of a road scheme. In this example only one line has been used for extended activities, the upper line depicting completion. As the slope of an activity gives the rate of

Table 9. Check-list of project constraints

Constraint	Description
Timing	Project start, finish and sectional completion dates.
Weather windows	Permitted paving season, normal earthmoving periods.
Weather restrictions	Low temperature periods, monsoon seasons.
Holidays	Public, trade, religious.
Access	Permitted access points to project, forbidden accesses, periods of favourable/unfavourable tides, railway possessions, river possessions, factory closures.
Environmental restrictions	Zones where restrictions may apply over noise, dust, weekend works and nightwork. Disturbance to protected flora and fauna.
Availability of key resources controlled by others	Major hired plant items, e.g. dredger, very heavy duty cranes. Labour, e.g. specialist subcontract groups.
Existing services	Overhead power lines, buried services, water, gas, telephone, TV, fuel oil.
Third parties	Works carried out by other contractors and statutory undertakers.

progress, an adjustable square becomes a useful planning tool. Having set the angle to suit the progress of a given gang, it is a simple movement to sketch in the effect of adding an additional gang to reduce an overrunning activity.

The second case study illustrates the use of the linear programme technique for a road scheme. The technique worked so well on the project that the linear programme was used for the contract programme and provided the basis for monitoring both by contractor and client. Linear programmes have been effective for numerous road projects, and also for a new single track railway extension, reconstruction of a multi-span viaduct, and replacement of quay heading.

Easter holiday 1989

Christmas holiday 1988

Deck

Bridge construction

7 Fill

7 Fill

16
15
14
13
11
10
9

7 + 8

17

Chalk settlement – 8 weeks

7 + 8 Earthworks fill

7 + 8

7 + 8

8
6 + 7
4

E4
4

5

21 Access 5

4

5

21 Access

2

1

All traffic flow maintenance 2-way

6000   6500   7000   7500   7600

E4   BT6 E5

Topsoil: 3750	Topsoil: 8500
Suitable: 6200	Suitable: 1250
U/S: 2100	U/S: 70
U/S below: 800	U/S below: 170

Rail

Lower fill: 6100	Lower fill: 55000
Upper fill: 2300	Upper fill: 27500
	Verge: 1450

1. Setting out	7. Lower fill	13. In situ channels
2. Site clearance	8. Upper fill	14. Road bases leanmix
3. Fencing	9. Drainage	15. Road base: flexible
4. Pre-earthwork drainage	10. Capping	16. Surfacing
5. Topsoil strip	11. Sub-base	17. Verge earthworks
6. Bulk earthworks	12. Kerbs and gullies	21. Accommodation works

Fig. 25. Part of a linear programme for a trunk road scheme showing activities from chainage 5500 to 7600 from start up to week 50

50

Variations

The reader may have come across other variations of the technique. The system described in the preceding section was originally developed by one of the authors for planning a new rail re-alignment in East Africa after experimenting unsuccessfully with the use of network analysis. It was based on the method of operational train control used by controllers on the East African Railways system to plot train positions on a single line network. The futility of using network analysis for a project as linear as a single line railway has to be tried to be appreciated. The network diagram ends up as a huge ladder of activities from which it is difficult to deduce anything useful.

Similar systems have been developed independently elsewhere, usually by contractors. One of these puts the chainage axis at the top of the sheet and plots time downwards; this is often used for tunnels because it is considered by some to be a more realistic representation of the work.

Linear programmes to networks

When there is an insistence that the programme for a linear project be presented as a network derived bar chart or cascade diagram there is no need to abandon the linear programme as the planning technique. It is quite easy to draw a network from a linear programme and an example is given at the end of section 3.7.

3.7. Network analysis
Basic principles

Network analysis is a general term for a graphical planning technique which shows the project as a network of its activities linked together to show their interrelationships and sequence of execution. With the addition of estimates of activity duration, the diagram can be analysed numerically to determine the estimated project duration. This analysis also distinguishes between those activities whose timely execution is vital to the earliest completion of the project, and those which may be delayed for a specific time without causing delay in the project completion.

Network analysis provides

- a diagram in which the work method is made explicit: a logic diagram

51

- a means of estimating the project duration by calculation from the activity durations

- a method of calculation which identifies activities that have a critical effect on the project duration (hence the terms critical path method and critical path analysis which are sometimes used to describe this technique)

- a method of calculation which determines by how much non-critical activities may be delayed without causing a delay in project completion.

In practical project management, this last facility of network analysis is most important, because it provides an objective means of scheduling project activities to make the best use of the available resources.

Good guidance on the use of network analysis for project management is given in BS 6046.[9] The terms and symbols used in this section are taken from BS 6046, except where stated.

For historical reasons, network analysis diagrams may be drawn in two ways: either precedence or activity-on-arrow. Until recently activity-on-arrow networks (arrow diagrams) were more popular in the UK and USA, whereas precedence was more popular in, for example, Australia. Precedence diagrams are now beginning to become more popular in the UK and seem likely to replace arrow diagrams eventually. Although the relative merits of each form are quite finely balanced (and BS 6046:1981 Part 2[9] gives an excellent comparative analysis), precedence diagrams are usually found to be easier for those who are new to the technique. Therefore, in this guide the precedence form is described first, and arrow diagrams are offered as an alternative. The technique will be described by means of its application to the construction of a small pumping station.

Pumping station example

Figure 26 shows a simple chamber used in land drainage. Porous land drains are laid in the land to be drained, and lead to a chamber with an automatic, submersible electric pump. The water is pumped to a convenient point of disposal, or to the next chamber in a line of chambers, controlled by an automatic system in the control box. The control box is also the termination point of the

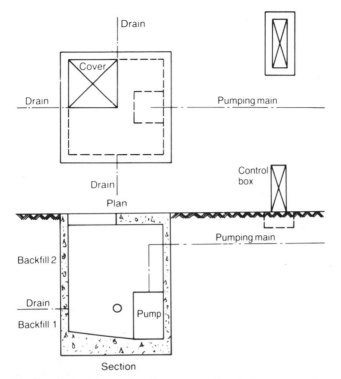

Fig. 26. Land-drainage chamber: **chamber** *is 3 m square internally*

incoming power supply, which is then connected to the pump from the control box.

Activities and work method

The activities for the construction of the chamber are given in Table 10. The construction method is given in the following, and is shown in network analysis form in Fig. 27.

Activity 1 (piling) is necessary because the chamber will obviously be constructed in waterlogged ground. These piles will be lightweight, and will be inserted with fairly light equipment. This will be the first activity, because little can be done until it is finished. The drains will have been laid in the fields previously, but will have been terminated about 5 m short of the chamber to avoid being damaged by the piling. Thus Fig. 27 shows this first activity proceeding on its own. It is expected to take 2 days to complete.

53

Table 10. Activity list for land-drainage chamber

Activity	Work involved
1. Piling	Install light steel piles to support excavation.
2. Excavate	Excavate, support piles, blind bottom.
3. Floor	Reinforcement, formwork, concrete to floor.
4. Control box base	Reinforcement, etc., to control box base.
5. Walls	Reinforcement, formwork, concrete to walls.
6. Roof	Reinforcement, etc., to roof, including cover.
7. Backfill 1	Backfill to underside of drains.
8. Drains	Make drain connections.
9. Pump	Install pump and connect to main.
10. Backfill 2	Complete all backfill and top soil.
11. Control box	Install control box and electricity supply.
12. Fencing	Fencing, gate and seeding.

Activity 2 (excavation) follows immediately after the completion of the piling. Fig. 27 shows this sequence, the arrow between activities 1 and 2 meaning that the piling must be wholly completed before the excavation can begin. The arrow joining the right-hand side of the box for activity 1 and the left-hand side of this activity is known as a finish-to-start dependency. As the excavation proceeds downwards, frames are installed to support the piling, and when the design depth has been reached the bottom of the excavation is blinded with concrete. The excavation will be dewatered continually with a diaphragm pump. This activity is expected to take 6 days.

Activity 3 (floor) begins immediately after the completion of the excavation.

Activity 4 (control box base) can be started immediately after the completion of the main excavation working in parallel with activity 3. It could, of course, have been started at the onset, because it is some distance from the main excavation so is not directly affected by it. Nevertheless, piling and excavation require the continual movement of construction machinery, which may damage the base. So the planner has decided not to begin this small piece of work until the excavation is complete.

Thus Fig. 27 shows how a network diagram indicates that *both* activity 3 and activity 4 *may begin* immediately after the completion of activity 2. Of course, more generally, an activity may have

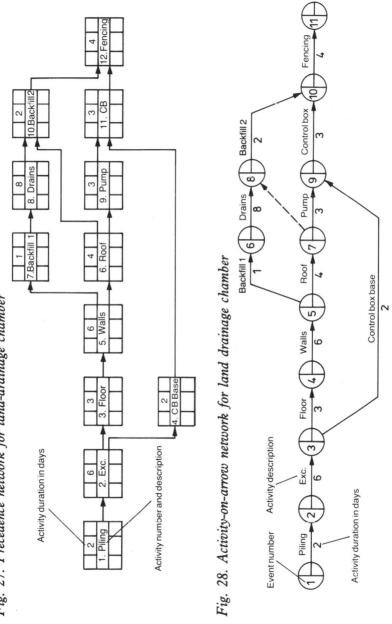

Fig. 27. Precedence network for land-drainage chamber

Fig. 28. Activity-on-arrow network for land drainage chamber

a number of succeeding activities. It is important to note the use of the words *may begin*: if there are not enough resources to begin activity 4 immediately, it is fairly obvious that it may be delayed for a while without delaying the overall time for the completion of the chamber. On the other hand, it is also obvious that delay in starting activity 3 will delay the chamber completion date.

Activity 5 (walls) follows the completion of the floor, and is independent of the control box base (activity 4), and so may proceed at the same time.

Activity 6 (roof) may follow the completion of the walls; this activity includes the cover.

Activity 7 (backfill to underside of drains) is necessary before the drain connections can be made, and obviously the walls must be completed before the backfilling can start; these relationships are shown in Fig. 27.

Activity 8 (drains) can follow the backfill and compaction to the level of their undersides. These connections are usually made by withdrawing a single pile on the line of the drain, and making the connection in a short trench.

Activity 9 (pump) follows the completion of the roof. The cover in the roof slab must be large enough for the pump to be removed for maintenance or replacement, so it is easier, and more prudent, to wait until all the concrete work is finished and the chamber is cleaned out before installing this piece of equipment.

Activity 10 (backfill 2) cannot start until the drain connections are complete, and also it obviously cannot be done before completion of the roof. These preceding dependencies are shown by the finish-to-start links between activities 6 and 10, and 8 and 10.

Activity 11 (control box) is installed by the supplier, who places it on its base, connects it to the pump and also to the mains electricity supply.

Activity 12 (fencing) cannot be done until the completion of the backfilling and topsoil replacement. It is shown following the installation of the control box, although in practice these two activities could proceed together. Indeed, for security reasons it may be necessary to complete the fencing before installing the control box, but because fencing must follow backfill 2, this would result in an extension of the project duration.

Thus Fig. 27 shows how a network analysis diagram may be used to illustrate a planned construction method.

Arrow diagrams: an alternative form of network

Figure 28 shows the activity-on-arrow diagram for the same construction method. The essential difference is that the activity is depicted by an arrow, rather than a box. The numbered circles at each end of the arrow are called events; these represent a point in time when *all* the preceding activities have been completed and all the following activities may be started. (This definition is important, as will be seen later in this section on the calculation of float.) Thus event 3 shows that point in time when the excavation is complete and both floor and control box base may be started; event 9 shows that the pump should have been installed and the control box base completed, so the control box supplier may start work. Note that the length of the arrow is not related to the activity duration, which has not yet been estimated; in fact it would be much more difficult to draw a diagram in this way.

The dotted arrow 7−8 shows that the roof must be complete before the backfilling may start; this dependency is the same as the finish-to-start link shown in Fig. 27 between activity 6 (roof) and activity 10 (backfill). This dotted activity is known as a dummy activity. It is necessary because the arrow diagram uses arrows to show both activities and the sequence of work. Thus the number of dependencies that may be shown will be related to the number of activities, and in most cases this number will be insufficient to show all the logical interrelationships in the work method. The dummy activities have zero duration and consume no resources, but otherwise are given the same treatment as the other activities. The need to introduce this contrivance is one of the weaknesses of arrow diagrams compared with precedence diagrams, because in precedence diagrams interrelationships can be introduced at will, with no need for dummies.

Otherwise, the two forms of network apply the same principles, as a comparison of Figs 27 and 28 will make clear.

Activity durations and resource assumptions

When drawing line-of-balance and linear programme diagrams, it is necessary to consider activity durations at the outset; the diagrams just cannot be drawn without this information. Also when bar charts are drawn directly for simple projects, it will be seen that it is again necessary to estimate the activity durations before the chart can be drawn.

57

One of the powerful attributes of network analysis is that the work method (logic diagram), resources required and activity durations may be considered separately, although ultimately they are all interrelated. The advantage is that the planner may consider one of these components of the plan at a time, rather than all at once. In planning the construction of the land-drainage chamber it has been seen that the work method can be shown in network form without considering what resources will be needed, except in the case of the sheet piles which are an intrinsic part of the work method. The number of men, machines, etc., has not yet been considered; i.e. it has been assumed that the availability of resources is infinite for the initial network plan. This assumption will enable the planner to use network analysis as a means of deciding on the resource levels required, rather than making assumptions at the beginning. Logical dependencies which express such resource-dependent reasoning as 'when this gang has finished this activity it can move to ... ' must be avoided, because the resulting network will be a confused amalgam of construction method and resource allocation. The importance of this principle will become clear in the resource analysis section.

Estimation of activity durations

Some guidance on estimating durations has already been given in section 2.7. At this stage in the plan, the duration of an activity should be estimated assuming that the resources allocated to it will be those normally used. Any consideration of ways of accelerating progress should be left until the critical activities have been identified, so that the commitment of additional resources will produce the maximum benefits. The activity durations estimated for the land-drainage chamber are shown in Fig. 27, and also in Fig. 28.

Time analysis

The duration of the project may now be calculated from the durations of the individual activities and their interrelationships. The purpose of the time analysis is to determine

(a) the estimated duration for the project
(b) the earliest start time for each activity (and so the earliest finish time)
(c) the latest start time (and latest finish time) for each activity

(d) from (b) and (c), the amount by which any activity may be delayed without delaying the project beyond the duration estimated in (a); that is, its float time.

The calculation for (a) and (b) is by the forward pass calculation; this is shown in Fig. 29. The calculation is made easier by using the convention that the project start date is day zero, although this may seem a strange assumption. The reason is that the calculations focus on the completion of an activity; for example, an activity of two days estimated duration would be completed at *the end of the second day*, if it started at *the beginning of the first day*. Thus its completion day is day 2, so to make the arithmetic work it must be considered to start *after the end of day zero* (i.e. the beginning of day 1), giving $0 + 2 = 2$. The use of this convention is generally considered to make the activity times look sensible, but it is only a convention.

The *forward pass analysis* is quite simple. Activity 1 (piling) starts after the end of day zero, is of two days duration and therefore will be complete at the end of day 2. From the network logic, activity 2 (excavation) may then start (after the end of day 2) and is to be completed six days later (at the end of day 8). Both activity 3 (floor) and activity 4 (control box base) may then start, after the end of day 8; and so the calculation continues. Early start times and early finish times are inserted in the top corners of the activity boxes, as indicated in Fig. 29. When two linking arrows converge on an activity, as with activity 10 (backfill 2), the network logic demands that *both* preceding activities must be complete before the activity may start. Thus although the preceding activity, number 6 (roof), will be complete by the end of day 21, activity 10 (backfill 2), will still have to wait until the completion of the other preceding activity, number 8 (drains), i.e. until after the end of day 26. Thus the rule for calculation of the earliest start time of activities that have more than one preceding activity is to take the *latest preceding finish time*. The forward pass also establishes the expected project duration time, in this case 32 days.

The *backward pass* establishes the latest start and finish time for each activity, and so works backwards from the end. For activities which have only one preceding activity, the latest start time is simply the latest finish time less the activity duration (the last activity takes the project time as its latest finish time). Where an

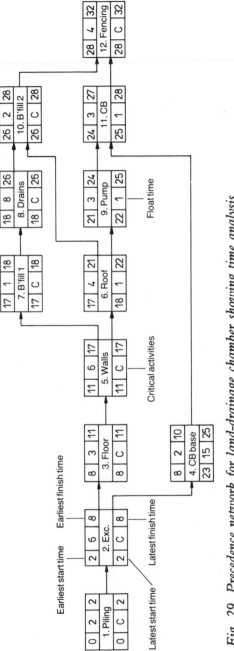

Fig. 29. Precedence network for land-drainage chamber showing time analysis

activity has more than one succeeding activity, the calculation involves making a choice; for example, the latest finish time of activity 6 (roof) could be either day 26 (from activity 10) or day 22 (from activity 9). Of course, it has to be day 22, the earliest time, because sufficient time must be allowed for the completion of the chain of activities 9–11–12 as well as the chain 10–12. Thus in the backward pass, the latest finish time of an activity is the *earliest of the latest start times of all the succeeding activities*. A simple reminder is 'take the latest time going forward, the earliest coming back'.

Thus the critical activities can be readily identified. Where the earliest start time and the latest start time are the same (and for precise definition, also the earliest and latest finish times are the same) the activity is obviously *critical*; that is, any delay beyond its earliest dates will delay the whole project. These activities are marked with a 'C' as shown. Activities that are not critical have what is called float.

Analysis of float

The determination of float may be done by

● drawing a bar chart from the network, or

● calculation.

The first method is time consuming but enables float to be interpreted more easily; the second is quicker and is often done by computer.

Figure 30 shows a bar chart drawn from the network shown in Fig. 29. The method is to plot the earliest start time for each activity, followed by a bar showing its duration; thus the end of the bar is the earliest finish time. The latest finish time is also plotted, and an outline bar shown from the earliest finish to the latest finish, which crudely represents float (note that BS 6046 shows the float as a line of dots, which is not such an effective illustration of float). These outline bars show the amount by which each activity may be delayed without delaying the earliest project completion date, but this does not mean that some other activities will not be delayed. A more specific definition of float is now required.

There are three types of float, and these will be illustrated by

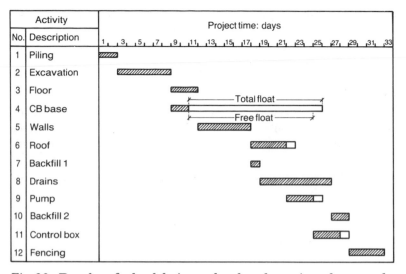

Fig. 30. Bar chart for land drainage chamber, drawn in early start order

means of activity 4 (control box base). *Total float* is the latest finish time of an activity, less the earliest start time, less the activity duration. For activity 4, this is $25 - 8 - 2 = 15$ days.

The outline bar in Fig. 30 is of 15 days' duration, and the method described earlier for drawing the bar chart gives the total float (if any).

Free float is the amount by which an activity may be delayed without delaying *any* subsequent activity beyond its earliest start time. For activity 4, there is only one succeeding activity, number 11 (control box), with an earliest start date of day 24. The earliest finish of activity 4 is day 10, so it may be delayed by $24 - 10 = 14$ days of free float before the delay would have any effect on activity 11 (control box). This is shown in Fig. 27. Stated more formally, free float is the earliest start time of *any* succeeding activity, less the activity early start time, less the activity duration; e.g. for activity 4, it is $24 - 8 - 2 = 14$ days.

Independent float is the float which will be available to an activity if all preceding activities are delayed until their latest finish, *and* no succeeding activity is to be delayed beyond its earliest start date. It is the earliest start date of *any* succeeding activity, less the latest finish date of *any* preceding activity, less the activity duration. For activity 4, this is $24 - 8 - 2 = 14$ days. The float calculations for the whole of the land-drainage chamber network are given in Table 11, and the float is drawn in Fig. 30.

A more rigorous definition of a critical activity can now be given; an activity is critical if it has no float.

Practical use of float

At face value, independent float is the most useful form of float, because it is the float available to an activity independent of the movements of preceding and subsequent activities within their own float. Unfortunately, as one would suspect, this happy state of affairs seldom occurs, so in most cases calculation of independent float is a futile exercise.

Free float is also attractive for scheduling purposes, and fortunately it occurs fairly frequently. A useful short-cut in manual calculation is to ignore all activities in chains of simple follow-on activities, except the last activity, because these can never have free float. Fig. 31 illustrates this; the float calculations are given in Table 12.

Table 12 illustrates the way in which the definition of free float makes it impossible for it to occur within an unconstrained chain of activities; and also that total float in such a chain is also shared float. The total float in the network is 4 × 60 = 240 units, which

Table 11. Float calculations for land-drainage chamber: days

Activity	Duration	Total float*	Free float	Independent float
1. Piling	2	$2-0-2=0$	$2-0-2=0$	$2-0-2=0$
2. Excavation	6	$8-2-6=0$	$8-2-6=0$	$8-2-6=0$
3. Floor	3	$11-8-3=0$	$11-8-3=0$	$11-8-3=0$
4. Control box base	2	$25-8-2=15$	$24-8-2=14$	$24-8-2=14$
5. Walls	6	$17-11-6=0$	$17-11-6=0$	$17-11-6=0$
6. Roof	4	$22-17-4=0$	$22-17-4=0$	$22-17-4=0$
7. Backfill 1	1	$18-17-1=0$	$18-17-1=0$	$18-17-1=0$
8. Drains	8	$26-18-8=0$	$26-18-8=0$	$26-18-8=0$
9. Pump	3	$25-21-3=1$	$24-21-3=0$	$24-22-3=1†$
10. Backfill 2	2	$28-26-2=0$	$28-26-2=0$	$28-26-2=0$
11. Control box	3	$28-24-3=1$	$28-24-3=1$	$28-25-3=0$
12. Fencing	4	$32-28-4=0$	$32-28-4=0$	$32-28-4=0$

*Obviously activities with no total float cannot have any other form of float. The calculations are given for illustration only.

†It is possible to obtain negative independent float (but not negative total or free float). This is meaningless and is taken as zero. Plotting activity 9 (pump) as a bar chart will illustrate the cause of this.

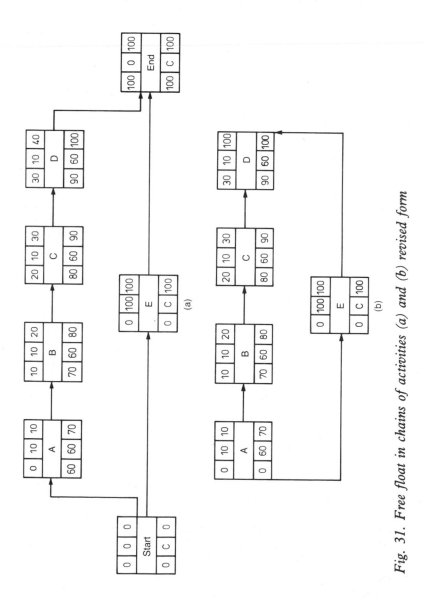

Fig. 31. Free float in chains of activities (a) and (b) revised form

Table 12. Float calculations for **Fig.** *31: arbitrary units*

Activity	Duration	Total float	Free Float
A	10	70 − 0 − 10 = 60	10 − 0 − 10 = 0
B	10	80 − 10 − 10 = 60	20 − 10 − 10 = 0
C	10	90 − 20 − 10 = 60	30 − 20 − 10 = 0
D	10	100 − 30 − 10 = 60	100 − 30 − 10 = 60
E	100	100 − 0 − 100 = 0	100 − 0 − 100 = 0

must indicate some sharing in a network of 100 units duration. Obviously, if activity A is delayed by the whole of its 60 units of float, then activities B, C and D will lose their float. It is important, therefore, to refer to the network diagram when interpreting float, and not to rely just on the figures in the calculation table.

Sensible meaning has to be attached to the word critical. For example, if an activity of four months' duration has one day of float, it is effectively critical.

Time analysis and arrow diagrams

The principles of network analysis are common to both forms of network. So the calculations shown in Fig. 32 are essentially the same as those shown in Fig. 29. However, the meaning attached to the figures in the diagram is different. In precedence diagrams, the box represents the activity and the four time figures in the box show the earliest and latest start times and the earliest and latest finish times, *of that activity*. In arrow diagrams, the figures show the *earliest and latest times of the event*. Remembering that an event shows a point in time when *all* the preceding activities have been completed, and *all* the succeeding activities may then start, it is clear that the figures given in the event circle refer only to a single point in time — not necessarily start and finish times of all the activities involved. Thus the calculation of float is different, but based on exactly the same definitions as for precedence diagrams.

Total float is the latest event time for the activity, less the earliest event time, less duration. Thus for activity 3−9 (the control box base, precedence activity 4) this calculation is $25 − 8 − 2 = 15$ days.

Free float is easier with arrow diagrams, because the earliest event time at the end of the head event (i.e. the event at the head of the arrow) is in fact the earliest start time of any subsequent activity;

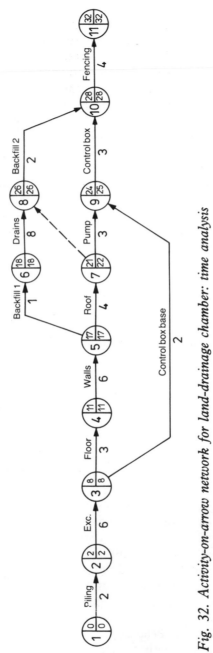

Fig. 32. Activity-on-arrow network for land-drainage chamber: time analysis

hence the free float for activity 3—9 is 24−8−2 = 14 days. This is the earliest time of the head event, less the earliest event time of the tail event, less the activity duration.

Independent float is similarly simplified by the use of the concept of event time: it is the earliest event time of the head event, less the latest event time of the tail event, less the activity duration. For activity 3—9, it is 24 − 8 − 2 = 14 days.

Thus in some ways float calculations are easier for arrow diagrams than for precedence diagrams, but again the need to use the dummy activity weakens the case for arrow diagrams. Float calculations for the dummy 7−8 will give a total float of 5 days. In this case the float calculated for a dummy actually refers to the preceding activity and its relationship with activity 8−10; this makes the interpretation of float more difficult.

Variations

Overlapping activities. Until now, all the networks shown have assumed that the whole of an activity must be complete before a succeeding activity may start. In practice, it is often the case that when some progress has been made on one activity, a succeeding

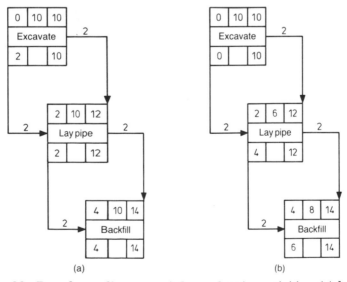

(a)   (b)

Fig. 33. Precedence diagrams with overlapping activities: (a) leads and (b) lags

activity may start. Fig. 33(a) shows a network for a pipeline in three simple activities: excavate trench, lay pipes, backfill. The arrows drawn show start-to-start relationships (between the start of two activities) and finish-to-finish relationships, showing relationships between the end of two activities. The numbers on these arrows represent leads for start-to-start relationships, and lags for finish-to-finish. The interpretation of this diagram is that the pipelaying may start two days after the start of excavation, and the backfilling after a further two days. Obviously, some equivalent constraint must be attached to the completion of these activities, because the excavation must be complete two days before the pipelaying can be completed, and the pipe must be laid two days before backfilling can be completed.

The analysis of lead and lag relationships follows the normal rules of the forward and backward pass calculations. This is quite straightforward for Fig. 33(a) but more difficult for Fig. 33(b). For example, the activity 'lay pipe' has an early start time of day 2, because it may start two days after the start of the activity 'excavate trench'. Its earliest finish is either its earliest start time plus duration ($2 + 6 =$ day 8) or, from the lag relationship, two days after the end of the preceding activity ($10 + 2 =$ day 12). Following the rules of the forward pass, the earliest finish time is day 12. The backward pass applies similar principles, using the earliest times.

Leads and lags do have the advantage that they may be usd to represent reality more closely, but the interpretation of the analysis becomes more complex. For example, the activities 'lay pipe' and 'backfill' in Fig. 33(b) clearly have a critical completion date, but there is some float attached to their start time. This may represent reality quite well, but confuses the definition of float! This is shown in Fig. 34 and this can be called preceding float.

A further illustration of start-to-start and finish-to-finish relationships is given in Fig. 31(b).

Summary or hammock activities. These are used either: to summarize part of the network or a subnetwork, for inclusion in a higher level plan at a lower level of detail; or to represent activities such as 'maintain site offices', the duration of which is dependent on the duration of the actual project activities. The difference between these activities and normal activities is that their duration is not assigned to them directly, but is drawn from the duration

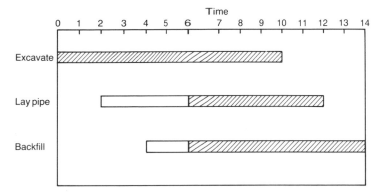

Fig. 34. Bar chart for Fig. 31 showing float available at start but not at end (concept of preceding float)

of the activities between the start and end of the summary or hammock. If changes are made to this part of the network, the duration must be revised. Computers do this automatically for activities designated as hammocks or summaries.

Figure 35 shows a summary activity for the land-drainage chamber. The project will include a number of these chambers, so the master programme will show the summary activities only. The term summary is used for these activities, for obvious reasons; the term hammock is usually applied to the overhead cost usage, where the activity is suspended, like a hammock, between the relevant physical activities.

Networks for repetitive construction. Network analysis diagrams do not lend themselves easily to repetitive construction, but a simplified approximation may be given using a ladder network. This enables a detailed plan for a repetitive part of a project, done by line-of-balance, to be incorporated into a higher level master programme done as a network.

Figure 36 shows how the plan for the ten repetitive houses given in the line-of-balance example may be converted to a ladder network; this is shown in arrow diagram form. The term ladder comes from the appearance of the diagram. The construction plan is simplified by showing the construction of each element for all the houses as a single activity; foundations becomes 50 days, that is ten foundations at five days each. (It is also possible to include the buffer times, by simply increasing the activity duration by this amount.) These combined activities form the rungs of the ladder.

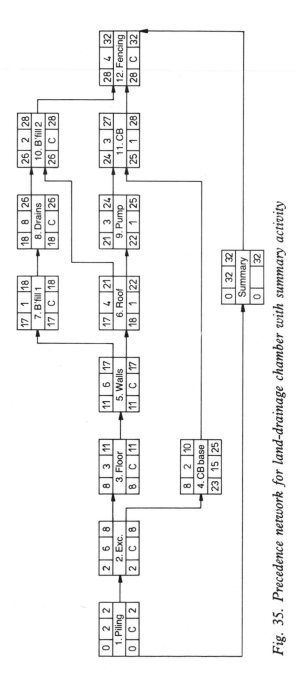

Fig. 35. Precedence network for land-drainage chamber with summary activity

Activity	Duration per house: days	Time for ten houses: days
1 — 2	5	50
3 — 4	8	80
5 — 6	6	60
7 — 8	3	30
9 — 10	5	50
11 — 12	2	20
13 — 14	4	40

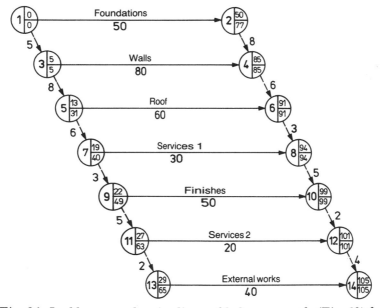

Fig. 36. Ladder network, using line-of-balance example (Fig. 19) for ten houses

Some provision must now be made to show an approximation to the sequence of work. This is done by using real time dummies for the first and last unit of each activity. Thus, the first wall cannot be started until the first foundation is complete. The foundation takes five days, so a real time dummy of this duration is inserted as shown. By similar logic, the event which says: 'both foundations and walls are now complete' must be preceded by a real time dummy for the walls of the last house. This dummy ensures that sufficient time is allowed for the walls of the last house to be completed after the completion of its foundations.

The resulting network is then analysed in the standard manner. Obviously, the walls are critical, and so is the timely completion of the succeeding activities, although there is some flexibility in their starting times. The interference problem which is central to the line-of-balance technique has not been considered, so the numerical results are different.

Ladders are a useful, but approximate device. Care must be taken when considering the analysis of resources.

Converting a linear programme to a network

It is not unusual for a client to specify that the contractor shall provide a network-derived bar chart. This is a common request

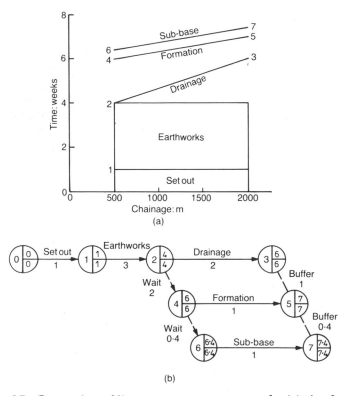

Fig. 37. Conversion of linear programme to network: (a) simple road scheme in linear programme format; (b) same scheme converted to a network

from management contractors who wish to incorporate each individual contractor's job network into the main project network. If the job is linear, there is no need to abandon the linear programme; both this technique and network analysis use timed activities and it is quite simple to transfer these from one format to the other.

The first stage is to identify each activity then number the beginning and end of each activity with event numbers as shown in Fig. 37(*a*). Activities need to be numbered in time sequence working from the bottom to the top of the time/chainage diagram. When all activities have been numbered, the network may be constructed. Where an activity begins immediately after the completion of the preceding activity as shown at events 1 and 2, set out/earthwork/drainage, the activity arrrows meet at the event nodes as shown on Fig. 37(*b*). When, however, waiting or buffer time has been introduced between activities, as between drainage 2−3 and formation 4−5, it is necessary to use real-time dummy activities in the network to maintain the logic.

Although an arrow network has been chosen to illustrate the conversion, in practice it is simpler to use a precedence diagram which does not require dummy activities. This procedure may appear tedious, but with very little practice it is possible to become quite adept at the conversion. A planner used to entering data by a keyboard will be able to transfer data directly onto the computer after the initial event numbering operation. The planner will not need to actually draw the network in Fig. 37(*b*) but will let the computer draw it for him.

4 Resources

One of the important objectives of planning is the efficient use of resources. This chapter gives an explanation of the techniques of resource analysis, and gives guidance on methods of resources scheduling. The important human aspects of resources planning are explained.

A major benefit of methodical and effective planning is the means it provides for the efficient control of resources. The basic construction resources are often called the four Ms: men, machines, materials and money. There are others: time is an important resource, as is the construction site itself, which like all other resources must be used to maximum effect. And, of course, good weather is an invaluable resource; a resource with seasonal availability which must be recognized at the strategic level of planning. The principal focus of managerial attention must, nevertheless, be the four Ms and time, and these resources will be the main subject of this chapter. The management of these resources will be developed in chapter 5.

The construction industry often operates at very low levels of net profit (of the order of 2—4% of turnover) so it cannot easily tolerate inefficiency in the use of resources. An example of resource use on a typical competitive civil engineering project is shown in the first two columns of Table 13.

It can be seen from the third and fourth columns that 5% unforeseen wastage on materials, or a 10% subcontractor's claim or 7% overuse of labour and plant will swallow up the net profit. As, unfortunately, resource overusage of this order is quite easily achieved, the careful management of resources must be a prime requirement of the planning process.

Of the four planning techniques that make up the planner's tool-kit, network analysis lends itself most readily to comprehensive resource analysis. In the line-of-balance technique, and to a lesser extent in linear programming, making effective use of resources is an integral part of drawing up the chart, and further analysis is not easy.

This chapter concentrates on resources analysis of plans derived from networks; a similar but less specific analysis may be based on bar charts. The analysis will be explained using the example of the land-drainage chamber which was used to explain network analysis in chapter 3.

4.1. Estimation of resource requirements

The estimate of the resources required for the construction of the chamber is given in Table 14. This is a very simplified estimate for this simple example. In practice, this estimate may be made in more detail, and the plan may be refined to overlap some

Table 13. Swallowing the profit margin, showing four common areas of inefficiency, any one of which will totally swallow up the 2% profit margin

Resources	Percentage of project value	Common inefficiences	Consequent effect on project
Materials	40	5% overuse due to losses, contamination overexcavation and short deliveries.	40% × 5% = 2% loss
Subcontractors	20	10% extra cost due to dayworks claims, waiting for materials and instructions.	20% × 10% = 2% loss
Labour	18 }	7% overuse due to bad planning, failure to put plant off hire.	28% × 7% = 2% loss
Plant	10 }		
Overheads	10	20% under-recovery due to project over-run, inflation, and estimating errors.	20% × 10% = 2% loss
Net profit	2		

activities to achieve more efficient use of some of the resources. Resources can be planned in either of two ways.

- On the basis that a finite number of each resource must be available for each and every period — this is the method shown in Table 14.

- In the form of total amounts for an activity, e.g. man-days, money etc.; in Table 14, the allocation of three men to activity 1 (piling) is equivalent to the allocation of six man-days for this activity of two days duration.

Usually in construction, site resources are planned on the basis of the allocation of a finite number of resources to an activity (first method) because this enables estimates to be made of maximum manning and equipment levels, which is essential for planning site accommodation, plant servicing and so on. The second method is used for financial planning.

4.2. Resource analysis

Resource analysis is concerned with making the best use of resources in the time-scale of the project, so the analysis must be done on a time basis. Therefore, the network is usually redrawn

Table 14. Resources for land-drainage chamber*

Activity	Labour	Carpenters	Sheet piles (set)	Wall forms (set)	Tractor shovel	Pump
1. Piling	3	—	1	—	1	—
2. Excavation	3	—	1	—	1	1
3. Floor	3	2	1	—	—	1
4. Control box base	1	2	—	—	—	—
5. Walls	3	2	1	1	—	1
6. Roof	3	2	1	—	—	1
7. Backfill 1	2	—	1	—	1	1
8. Drains	2	—	1	—	1	1
9. Dewatering pump	1	—	1	—	—	—
10. Backfill 2	2	—	1	—	1	—
11. Control box†						
12. Fencing	2	—	—	—	—	—

*Reinforcing steel will be fixed by labour-only subcontractors.
†Installed by specialist subcontractor.

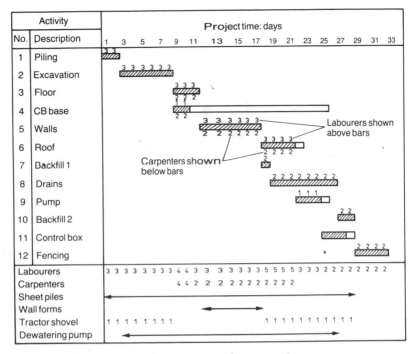

*Fig. 38. Resource requirements, **early** start order*

in the form of a bar chart, and resources allocated in the way shown in Fig. 38. The resource requirements estimated to be required for each activity are shown in Table 14.

There are three forms of resource analysis: resource aggregation; resource smoothing; and resource levelling.

Resource aggregation

Resource aggregation is shown in Fig. 38. This is the simple summation of the total number of each resource required by the activities planned, for each period. Care has to be taken with items such as the sheet piles and the pump, because these are required to maintain the excavation in good order throughout most of the construction. So these items must be allocated to activities such as walls although they are not directly concerned with wall construction. (As an alternative, such resources can be shown in the network itself as hammock activities; e.g. sheet piles would be a hammock from the start of the piling activity to the completion of the backfill activity.)

Resource smoothing

Resource smoothing may be used to make the pattern of resource demand given by the aggregation more manageable, *but without extending the planned project duration.* The technique is to delay some of the activities within their respective float, to remove peaks of resource demand. The objective is to produce a schedule that requires a steady and more or less constant demand for a particular resource (a smoothed resource), because generally it is difficult to manage a resource for which demand fluctuates between very different levels.

A simple illustration of smoothing is given in Fig. 39 where the delay of activity 4 has given a smooth demand for carpenters, and an improved, but still imperfect, demand for labourers. Obviously, the scope for smoothing resources demand is limited by the float available and the constraints expressed by the network.

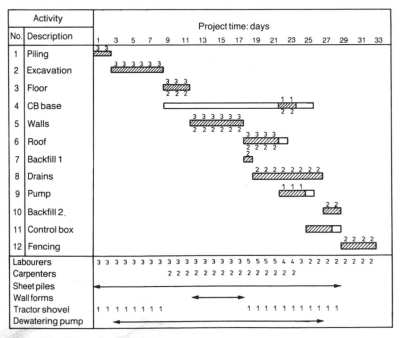

Fig. 39. Smoothed resources

Resource levelling

Resource levelling reschedules the project activities to give a maximum demand for each resource within an imposed limit. This may cause the project to be delayed, if the resources made available are insufficient to reschedule the activities within the float available. Fig. 40 shows a schedule for levelled resources, with an imposed limit of three labourers and two carpenters. The first problem occurs with the roof (activity 6) and backfill 1 (activity 7) because to schedule them concurrently would require 3 + 2 = 5 labourers. Because the roof is the longest and most expensive of the two activities, and is also a critical activity, it is sensible to delay the backfill, and allocate the resources to the roof. Delay of activity 7 from day 18 to day 22 must delay the next activity in the network, activity 8; originally starting after day 18, it now starts four days later. This activity is critical, yet has been delayed by the resource levelling process; this is an illustration of the effect of scheduling with imposed resource restraints. Clearly, in the levelling process, the original critical path concept evaporates; resources are now allocated to activities on the basis of the importance of

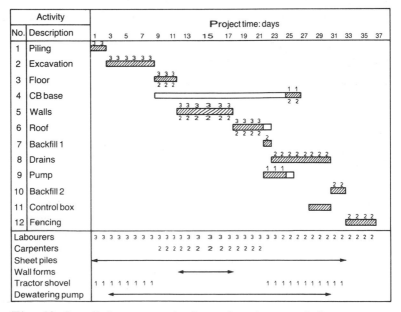

Fig. 40. Levelled resources (project duration extended)

the activity itself to the completion of the project, by a new system of priorities. For example, when a choice has to be made between two or more activities which require the same resource, it may be best to allocate the resource to the activity with the longest duration, or the earliest start, or by some other rational priority. Alternatively, the project manager may assign priorities to activities on the basis of a 1–10 scale, and this may form the basis for decision making in conditions of limited resources.

Continuing the levelling, the delay of the drains then delays backfill 2 (activity 10) and the fencing (activity 12). The project duration has been extended by four days (from 32 days to 36 days).

In this example the process was applied to just one resource, labourers. Fortuitously, the demand for carpenters is unaltered, but the sheet-piles are required for an extra four days, and so is the dewatering pump. Thus an improvement in the schedule of one resource (in this case labour) has resulted in the schedule for another two resources to be made less economic. This is the fundamental problem with resource scheduling, and the final schedule will almost always be a compromise. It is in the process of searching for an effective resource schedule that skilled and experienced planners can make a really important contribution to the efficiency of construction.

4.3. Other forms of presentation

The resource demand schedule is shown in Figs 38–40 as a simple strip of numbers (e.g. labourers 3 3 3 etc.). This form of presentation is quite adequate for most practical purposes, and has the advantage of being very compact. An alternative form is to plot these figures in diagrammatic form, as a vertical bar chart or histogram. Examples of computer drawn histograms are given in the third case study.

A further refinement is the cumulative resources curve, shown in Fig. 41. The graphs show the cumulative demand for labourers and carpenters, in man-days. Curves of this type form a basis for project monitoring and control, which is described in chapter 5. The curve shown in Fig. 41 is derived from the original early-start bar chart, and a further refinement is to plot on the same axes a similar curve based on a late-start schedule. This is shown in a general way in Fig. 42. The difference between the two lines is called the float envelope; this is the envelope of the resource

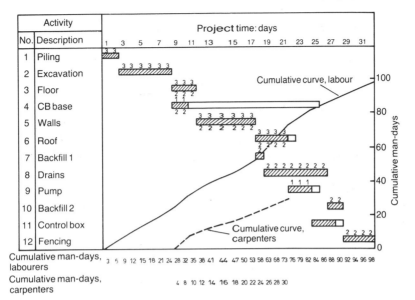

Fig. 41. Cumulative resource curves for labour and carpenters, early start

demand for the resource under consideration for all the ways of resource smoothing; i.e. for all schedules that do not delay the project completion from that originally calculated.

4.4. Planning for effective scheduling

These analyses demonstrate why it is best to assume that infinite resources are available when first drawing the network diagram. If resource limitations are implied in the constraints and these dependencies are shown on the original network diagram, the resource analysis becomes muddled between rescheduling the activity times and also having to change resource-based logic. It is far more effective to draw the network to express only physical constraints and engineering decisions, assuming infinite resource availability, and leave the introduction of resource constraints until the resource analysis. That is, the use of resources should be an *output* from the planning process, not an input. Normally, when major scarce resources are to be used, it would be foolish to assume infinite availability, so the work would have to be planned around them. Nevertheless, for general construction work, using generally available resources, the initial assumption of infinite availability

81

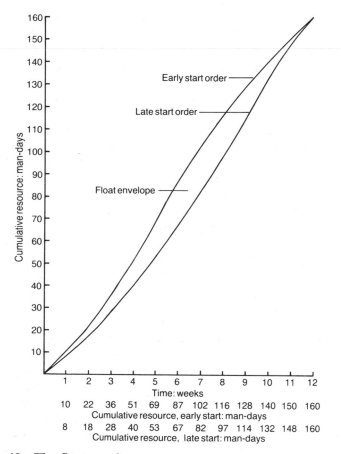

Fig. 42. The float envelope

should result in better resource schedules. Furthermore, it is clear that there will be more scope for the resource analysis to produce an economic schedule if the network is not unnecessarily complex. Logical relationships should be introduced into a network only after careful thought, because these will in turn constrain the options available to the scheduler. A very complex, tightly planned project will offer much less scope for the scheduler than a more loosely planned project with more activities running concurrently.

82

4.5. Scheduling systems

Most computer-based project management systems have a scheduling facility. These aim to produce schedules automatically, and are constructed around a system of rules (such as those given in the resource levelling part of section 4.2) to enable a best schedule to be identified. These automatic schedulers can be used to great effect, but they require skill and understanding from the user — that is, they must be used with caution.

It is often much more important that the project manager and planner produce a schedule which they have devised from a study of the construction work itself, and to which they have become personally committed, rather than strive for a theoretically optimum mathematically derived schedule. Schedules must appear sensible and practical to those who have to make them work. Generally, manual analysis will encourage the production of such schedules, but the use of computers to produce a new aggregation quickly and easily, after each activity is rescheduled by the planner, is beneficial and encourages experimentation. In many cases, using computers in this way may be more effective than using the automatic scheduler.

4.6. Resource scheduling and people management

The human aspects of resource scheduling are important. First, it is rarely practical to schedule the work of individual people. People usually work in groups — in project teams, office groups or, on site, in gangs. The formation and development of harmonious working groups is an important managerial task, so the scheduling of human resources must be based on groups rather than individuals. This practical reality results in schedules that are cruder than those based on scheduling individuals, thus simplifying a complex process. Second, human resources are capable of scheduling their own work. If management does not schedule the human resources and manage the implementation of these schedules, the human resources may make their own schedules to suit their own individual objectives and wishes; such schedules may have detrimental effects on the efficient scheduling of non-human resources such as plant and money. Thus schedules for human resources must aim to ensure that each group of people has a continuous programme of work, together with the necessary resources; and that they know that this is the case.

5 Monitoring and control

Planning lays the foundations for monitoring and control. Monitoring is required to establish what progress has been made against the plan. Control is taking corrective action. Simple methods of monitoring and control are given, based on the planning techniques already described.

Essentially, there are two ways to execute and control construction work. It may be let under contract to someone else, where control is exercised through the enforcement of the contact; in practice, this means the threat of penalty for non-performance, after the event. Alternatively, it may be executed and controlled directly with the help of some form of system. Monitoring and control will be discussed in the context of these alternatives.

When used in project management, the words monitoring and control are often used as if they were interchangeable. Computer systems for handling and reporting cost data are more likely to be called cost control systems than cost monitoring or costing systems. This terminology is unfortunate, because it can obscure the reality of project control by giving the impression that it can be done by some automatic, dispassionate and perhaps even painless process. In fact, there can be no such thing as a project control system. Project control is exercised by *managers*, and perhaps by other people, who take action which influences future events. Usually, the actions will be based on decisions made after a study of the facts; that is, on the results of some form of monitoring process. A formal and systematic monitoring process will form a management information system (MIS). A good MIS will provide managers with a sufficiently accurate statement of the current state of a project for making sensible decisions, and will also enable the manager to make a prediction of the likely results. Control and taking action must be based on authority and power. In most cases this is drawn from some form of contract. For example, clients may have the contractual right to charge their contractors liquidated damages if they run late and contractors will have the power to require subcontractors to remove defective work and repeat it properly. Contracts also place obligations and constraints on the parties to them.

It is quite useless to provide a project manager with information about something which he is powerless to influence, so the basis of authority — in practice the form and content of the contract — will determine the objectives and design of the MIS. Thus, before explaining the process of monitoring and control of construction work, it is necessary to describe the contractual framework. This begins with an analysis of the apportionment of the risks involved, because this is the basis of contract strategy.

5.1. Control of risk

Imagine that a port authority wishes to build a new container terminal. From a knowledge of the current shipping market, it

Table 15. Risks facing a port authority considering building a new terminal

Type of risk	Examples
Commercial	There may be a shipping recession. Another port may construct a more attractive terminal.
Disaster	The project may be delayed, damaged or destroyed a natural (or man-made) disaster.
Design	The terminal may not be efficient to operate. The terminal may prove to be structurally defective.
Cost overrun	Estimates of construction cost may be too optimistic. Efficiencies of workforce and construction plant may fall below acceptable levels.
Time overrun	Estimates of construction time may be too optimistic. The workforce may work inefficiently and take longer than the schedule allows.

is calculated that for the terminal to be economically viable, (i.e. to attract container business away from other ports), the construction costs must not exceed £10 million and the terminal must be operational within 18 months. The risks facing the port authority are summarized in Table 15.

The commercial risks will be borne by the port authority. Although it may seek specialist advice from experts in world trade and maritime affairs, the actual financial risks of a failure in commercial judgement will remain with the port authority. The risk of delay or damage from the effects of a disaster will almost certainly be covered by insurance, leaving the port authority with a number of choices, shown diagrammatically in Fig. 43, of how to apportion the remaining risks.

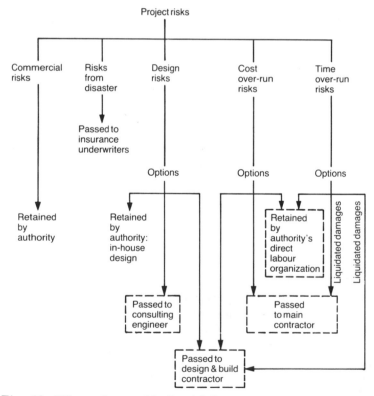

Fig. 43. Who ends up with the risks?

It is possible, but unlikely, that the port authority may choose to design and construct the terminal using its own resources; in this case it accepts the design, cost overrun and time overrun risks. If the authority is a large one operating a number of ports, it is likely that it will decide to accept the design risks by using its own designers but avoid the risks of cost and time overrun by having the construction done by a contractor.

The two remaining options are to pass the design risk to a consulting engineer and the construction risks to a contractor; or, to pass all three risks to a contractor with experience in the design and construction of such projects. Once the risk has been passed on to another party, as far as the port authority is concerned, it has been effectively controlled. This example illustrates that a contract is a device for controlling risks by passing those risks, for a consideration, to another party.

The first exercise in the control of risk is always to decide how much risk to *pass on* to others (by contract or subcontract) and therefore how much to *retain*. Having made that decision, those risks that remain must be monitored and controlled.

5.2. Client's control

The relationship between risk and control is best illustrated by a discussion of two extreme contract strategies, illustrated in Fig. 44. The fixed price, lump sum contract passes most of the risk

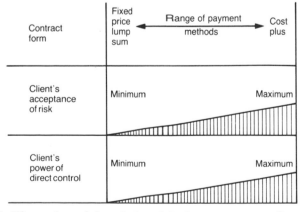

Fig. 44. Illustration of the relationship between contract form, control and risk

to the contractor. It also gives the contractor the right to control the execution of the work, and the data relating to cost are private to him. At the other extreme, in the case of the cost plus contract, the client reimburses the contractor for all direct expenses — the cost — and also charges for management and other overheads — the plus. In these cases, the risk is with the client, but so is the control because the client is free to direct the work as he wishes, and has direct access to cost information to help him make decisions.

In the fixed price, lump sum contract, the client can monitor progress but there is little that he can do to control it. In most cases, the contract will be an entire contract, for the delivery of the whole of the works on a specific date. There will be no practical provision in the contract for adjusting the price for changes or extra work, because these are not expected. This form of contract is analogous to firing a gun: the direction and speed of the bullet cannot be influenced after it has left the gun barrel; thus the client can monitor progress and technical performance only. Nevertheless, the client can manage the project: developing a good spirit of co-operation, ensuring that payments are made promptly. If progress falters the client and his representatives can influence the contractor by continually emphasizing the problems and persuading the contractor to take action.

In the case of contracts where the client maintains more direct control — cost plus being an extreme example — then the client has access to information on costs and resource usage, and so can use some of the management information systems used by construction contractors.

5.3. The contract programme

Most forms of contract require that the contractor will provide a programme for the complete project at an early stage, and that the programme shall be acceptable to the client. This contract programme forms the basis for assessing the progress of the project. In the standard form of civil engineering contract, this requirement is given in Clause 14, which states *inter alia*

> 14. (1) Within 21 days after the acceptance of his Tender the Contractor shall submit to the Engineer a programme for his approval showing the order of procedure in which he proposes to carry out the Works

and thereafter shall furnish such further details and information as the
Engineer may reasonably require in regard thereto. The Contractor shall
at the same time also provide in writing for the information of the
Engineer a general description of the arrangements and methods of construction which the Contractor proposes to adopt for the carrying out
of the Works.

(2) Should it appear to the Engineer at any time that the actual progress of the Works does not conform with the approved programme
referred to in sub-clause (1) of this Clause the Engineer shall be entitled
to require the Contractor to produce a revised programme showing the
modifications to the original programme necessary to ensure completion of the Works or any Section within the time for completion as
defined in Clause 43 or extended time granted pursuant to Clause 44(2).

The legal status of this programme is complex. It is not necessary
for the contractor to work to the programme. The contract requires
that the entire works be delivered on the specified date. The contractor is not required to deliver each item on the programme on
the date shown on that programme, because this would subdivide
the project into a number of projects. In this case, the defects
liability period for each part would start from the completion of
that part, rather than from the completion of the whole project,
which will give rise to administrative and financial difficulties.

Thus the contract programme can only be used to guide the
client's representatives on whether the actual progress achieved
at a particular time is sufficient to make it likely that the planned
completion date will be met. Of course, contractors who are behind
schedule will argue — often realistically — that they will catch up
later, so progress has to be quite substantially behind schedule
before the client can have any real influence on the contractor.

'Who owns float?' is another important issue in the contract programme. Take for example a case where due to an unusual technical
problem the client's engineer is late in providing the drawings for
an activity on the contract programme. The start of this activity
is delayed by three weeks. The contract programme is in the form
of a network, from which it is clear that this activity has four weeks
float. The engineer argues that there is therefore no problem, and
that he will not consider claims for the cost of the delay.

The contractor puts forward the counter-argument that he owns
the float, because of the entire nature of the contract, and he needs
this to make best use of his resources through systematic

scheduling. In the Authors' view, this argument is correct, especially in the case of well-organized contractors. Of course, quantifying a claim for the cost of delay on an activity with float will be very difficult, taking into account that the contractor will have a duty under common law to mitigate the effects of this delay. Despite this, the principle that the contractor owns the float must be respected, and clients should not rob him of this important managerial asset.

In turn, main contractors will not wish to pass float on to a subcontractor, because they will need this to juggle with the progress of all the subcontractors and the directly controlled work so as to achieve the desired overall result. Thus subcontractors will be given firm start and finish dates, and will be expected to plan their own activities so that their own plan includes adequate float.

5.4. Contractor's control

The contractor has to decide what work will be left to subcontractors and which he will do directly. If a subcontractor is used, the contractor becomes a client and much of what has been written about control by the client will apply to the contractor. If he uses his own resources, he must realize that each of the major categories of resources will have its own control characteristics, and must be managed in an appropriate way. Table 16 summarizes the ways of monitoring construction resources and makes some suggestions about ways in which they may be controlled.

Monitoring and control is the core activity of site management, and has to be done effectively and efficiently. There are three essential components

- collecting information about the actual achievements on the project

- processing this information into simple reports which compare planned and actual progress in a way which can be understood quickly

- taking necessary controlling action, replanning as necessary.

This is a cyclic, regular process, which requires persistence on the part of the managers and planners; it is illustrated by Fig. 45. It is essential to find some effective level of information gathering and processing which gives reasonably accurate and relevant infor-

Table 16. Ways of monitoring construction resources and costs

	Principal resources and costs	What can go wrong?	How can resource use be monitored?	Some possible control measures
Direct costs	Labour	Low output. Industrial action. Sickness and absenteeism	Regular cost/income comparisons. S-curves.	Replanning. Bonus systems. Enlightened management and welfare.
	Plant	Low output/ misuse. Breakdowns. Theft.	Regular cost/income comparison. S-curves.	Operator training. Preventive maintenance. Security marking.
	Materials	Waste. Overuse/misuse. Short measure. Theft.	Regular reconciliation of delivery and use. S-curves.	Delivery checks. Setting-out checks. Good housekeeping. Secure compounds.
	Subcontractors	Insolvency. Inefficiency. Incompetence.	Progress monitoring. Firm negotiating.	Financial and technical vetting before contract.
On-site overheads	Site staff	Too many/ too few. Inexperienced. Lack of skill and understanding.	Compare actual costs with forecast staff costs and other project staff costs.	Issue written job descriptions. Control manning. Practical training. Provide motivation.
	Site offices, equipment, transport, etc.	Full establishment remains on site after reduction of level of activity.	Compare time-related establishment cost with turnover.	Adjust establishment to suit turnover.
Off-site overheads	HQ office costs	Plenty, but not within the scope of this book.		
	Insurance	Poor damage and accident record pushes up premiums.	Accident reporting system.	Disciplinary measures for carelessness. Training.
	Finance costs	Heavy start-up costs not matched by early income. Client slow to pay.	Value-income monitoring.	Quicker certification. Rigorous credit control. Good client relations.

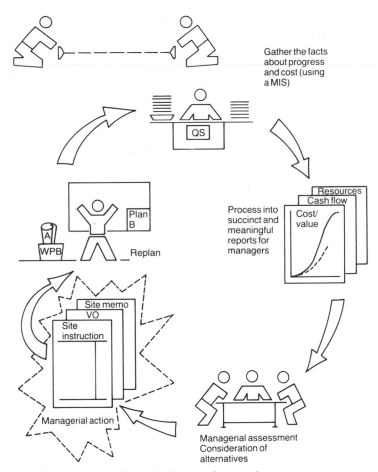

Fig. 45. The cycle of monitoring and control

mation without wearisome and time consuming effort. The methods given in this chapter may appear to be fairly simple, but experience has shown that they can be used effectively week-in, week-out, on most projects. To maintain very complex, detailed and notionally more accurate and precise systems has been found to consume so much effort that frequently the system falls into disuse (after an initial period of enthusiasm) leaving no monitoring and control system at all. A careful balance has to be struck between simplicity and accuracy. The Authors believe that more sophisticated systems should only be introduced after these simple systems have been established as working tools.

5.5. S-curves: the basic tool

Figure 42 illustrated how graphs may be drawn showing the cumulative amount of planned resources against time. If such graphs are drawn for actual projects, they usually have the characteristic S-shape shown in Fig. 46. This shape reflects the pattern of activity of most projects, which take time to gather momentum, have an intensive main period of activity when most of the resources are consumed, and a finishing-off period, when the level of activity dies away. S-curves may be drawn for people, money, materials such as concrete and other resources, and may thus form the basis for controlling the use of those resources. The overall progress of the project will be monitored by using total project costs and values, and it is this overall control chart which is shown in Fig. 46. Progress may also be assessed by monitoring a few key activities.

The basic cost/value S-curve shown in Fig. 46 is common to

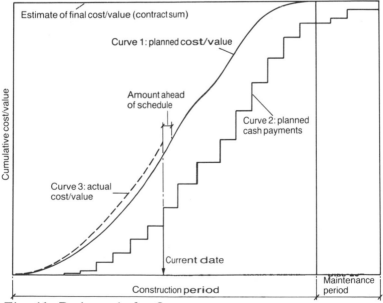

Fig. 46. Basic cost/value S-curve

both client and contractor. To the client it represents the rate at which the cost of the project will be incurred, and the amount and timing of the cash payments. To the contractor, it represents the rate at which the work will bring value to the firm, and also of course, the timing and amount of cash receipts.

Curve 1 is the cumulative cost or value of the work done day-by-day, according to the cost/value of each activity at its planned scheduled date. Curve 2 is calculated from curve 1 by interpreting the contract conditions for payment. Most construction contracts allow for the contractor to be paid for the work in stages, rather than in one single sum on completion. The contract defines the period of the valuation, the maximum time between valuation and payment, the amount of money to be retained by the client to safeguard his interests in case of the discovery of defective work, and other items such as payment for materials brought to the site but not yet used. This contractual information enables the planner to calculate the values for curve 2. Note that usually some of the retention money is repaid at the end of the construction period (on substantial completion) and the remainder after a maintenance period during which any defects which are revealed shall be corrected.

The cost/value curve is a convenient basis for assessing the overall progress of a project. Money is a common factor in all the numerous resources and activities in a project, and may be usually used as the common measure of progress (but see section 5.10).

Progress achieved at the end of each period may be assessed by valuing the work actually completed, in the same way in which the original planned value was computed. Thus curve 3 shows the cost/value of the work completed to date, period-by-period. Time is measured on the horizontal scale, so the amount by which the project is ahead of schedule may be read off the graph. The percentage of work complete is given by comparing the actual and planned cost/value as follows

$$\text{percentage complete} = \frac{\text{actual cost/value} \times 100}{\text{estimated final cost/value}}$$

Fig. 46 shows a project ahead of schedule, but the same principles apply, obviously, to projects behind schedule. Equally it is possible to revise the planned cash payments curve (curve 2) to reflect the actual progress, but this has been omitted for reasons of clarity.

94

From the discussion on client control given in section 5.2, it is possible that control curves of this type may satisfy the needs of a client entirely; they must be supported of course by explanation and interpretation.

5.6. Contractors' control curves

Progress monitoring is expensive. It requires a large proportion of the planner's time and also of those who will supply the information. Thus some effective level of detail has to be established, but, more importantly, the items that are to be monitored must be selected carefully. It is not economic to monitor everything, so the project manager must select those items for monitoring that will give him sufficient information to exercise control. For most projects control curves will be drawn for

- progress, cost/value comparions
- cash flow
- labour, perhaps with plant and equipment
- a few key activities
- a few key resources.

To most contractors, the comparison of cost and value, and the control of cash flow (which is the driving force of contractors) are crucial. Thus curves 1 and 2 are most important.

5.7. Control curve for progress and cost/value comparison

Figure 47 shows the general form of such curves. The planned accrued value curve is the same as curve 1 in Fig. 46. This gives the cumulative planned value of the work done. As the project proceeds, the actual value of the work done at a particular date may be estimated fairly accurately, and this may be plotted in a similar way, as in Fig. 46. The amount of time that the project is ahead of or behind schedule may be assessed. The addition of the cumulative total cost line will give an indication of profitability; care must be taken over the use of this term, because profit only has real meaning for the firm as a whole, not individual projects. Thus the word contribution is more generally used, meaning the contribution the project is making to the general overhead expense and profit of the firm, after deducting the direct project costs.

95

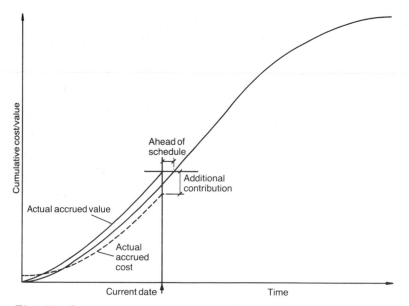

Fig. 47. Control curve for progress and cost/value comparison

This control curve is crucial to decision making. It is important that it is prepared speedily and promptly, usually monthly but often weekly. To achieve timely production of the chart, it is often necessary to use approximate or simplified data, rather than detailed and accurate figures. These charts are for decision making, where time is the essential factor. Of course prudence indicates that these systems are subsequently validated and corrected by more detailed management information systems.

5.8. Cash-flow curve

Figure 48 shows a cash-flow control curve. It is the same as Fig. 46 but with the addition of a curve showing the cumulative payments to suppliers (and the actual payments of other costs). Thus the difference between the planned payment line and the planned (i.e. expected) cash payments from the client gives the planned working capital requirement for the project. The maximum difference between these two figures is the maximum cash expected to be required by the contractor to run the project. The total area between the curves (shown shaded in Fig. 48) will be in units of money multipled by time and if multiplied by an appropriate interest rate (or, more correctly, cost of capital), then this will give a good indication of the expected cost of financing the project.

The computation of the *planned payments to suppliers line* will be difficult and tedious. It is often accurate enough (for control purposes) to make the approximation that this curve will follow the planned accrued value curve by a fixed delay — say four weeks. This fixed delay may be estimated from a study of a sample of actual payments made by the firm for major resources such as labour, plant, concrete, steel, bricks, etc. By noting the time difference between the date of use of these in the project, and the date when the payment was made, an estimate of the payment delay may be given by taking the weighted average of cost times payment delay. Such approximations may give timely information of sufficient accuracy for management decision making; the alternative may be to provide accurate information but to accept the necessary time delay.

With high interest rates and small profit margins, control of cash has become of paramount importance for the survival of many firms. The cash-flow curves shown in Fig. 48 can be used as a

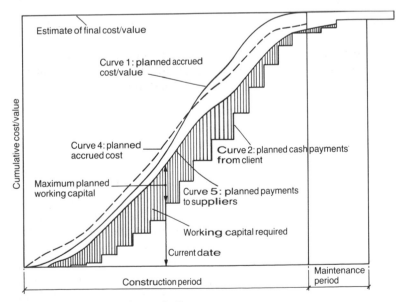

Fig. 48. Contractor's cash flow curve

basis for monitoring the actual cash flow, and for predicting future cash flows.

5.9. Control curves for labour, plant and equipment

Labour may be termed an active resource. However automated construction work becomes, machines will always be controlled by people. This active quality of labour content of a project means that manpower performance by itself is an indicator of the overall progress of the project. Thus control curves may be drawn for either man-hours or labour cost, and will take a similar form to Fig. 47.

Monitoring progress on the basis of man-hours is common practice in the oil, gas, process and petrochemical industries. Here a common procedure is as follows.

- As part of the tender conditions the contractor has to provide a detailed breakdown of the true man-hour content of his tender for monitoring progress. Even better, a man-hour-resourced network is used as a contract programme; this will enable a computer to be used for periodic monitoring.

- After tender award a monitoring bar chart is prepared, for example as shown in Fig. 49, to show the percentage of the total project that each activity represents; this is known as a weighting. These weightings are entered in a column on the bar chart, then each weighting is divided by the number of monitoring periods in the activity to arrive at a unit weighting.

o For example, given that the total project is to take 100 000 man-h, activity 1 (excavate foundations) is planned to take 10 000 man-h, its duration is two weeks, and that the monitoring period is one week, then

$$\text{weighting of activity 1} = \frac{10\ 000}{100\ 000} \times 100 = 10\%$$

$$\text{unit weighting (per week) of activity 1} = \frac{10\%}{2\ \text{weeks}} = 5\%\ \text{week}$$

- For each monitoring period, the unit weightings of all activities are summed and entered at the bottom of the chart. These progress sums may be plotted as a histogram or cumulatively as a programme S-curve.

	Activity	Weightings	Week						
			1	2	3	4	5	6	7
1	Excavate foundations	10	5	5					
2	Concrete foundations	15		7·5	7·5				
3	Columns	5			2·5	2·5			
4	Roof	30				15	15		
5	Floor	30					15	15	
6	Finishes	10							10
		100							
Programme week			5·0	12·5	10·0	17·5	30·0	15·0	10·0
cumulative			5·0	17·5	27·5	45·0	75·0	90·0	100·0
Progress week			4·0	10·0	10·0				
cumulative			4·0	14·0	24·0				

Fig. 49. Weighted man-hour progress chart

- To monitor progress it is necessary to assess the progress of each activity on a percentage basis. These percentages are applied to the activity weightings to produce progress weightings and the progress weightings summed to find how the project is progressing in terms of percentage of work complete. This percentage is plotted in comparison with the programme S-curve.

This procedure provides a visual comparison of S-curves and also an accurate progress percentage figure for reporting purposes.

In the offshore industry a number of individual projects, some geographically remote, may have to be progressed simultaneously to a common completion date. To have gas wells and pipelines ready to produce but unable to be commissioned because the on-shore reception facilities were incomplete would be unthinkable.

It is in these circumstances that the need for accurate and frequent monitoring is quickly understood and the increased costs of planning staff easily justified.

In his excellent book on the use of network analysis in project control, Albert Lester[10] describes an alternative to the weighting method, and develops this approach to progress monitoring in some detail. A graph of man-hours has the advantage of being independent of changes in wage rates or the value of money, but the use of cost is more realistic and makes it easier to integrate the labour data with other control data, which will be in monetary units. Plant and equipment may also be considered to be active resources, because they are used and controlled by people. It is these active resources which achieve progress on a project, and thus a control curve for labour, plant and equipment (in financial terms) will give a good measure of general progress.

5.10. Monitoring progress by key activities and resources

The physical progress of many civil engineering projects may be monitored by consideration of just a few items. For example, tunnelling is essentially about boring and lining; the construction of a concrete dam is essentially achieved by placing concrete. Curves comparing planned and actual achievement may be drawn and updated daily, giving a simple and immediate control tool.

5.11. Control of materials

In contrast to labour and plant, materials are a passive resource. They are subject to wastage, theft, decay and physical damage. They may be stockpiled, stored and, in some cases, reused. They require separate methods of control, and cannot be included in the general project monitoring and control systems described previously.

5.12. Monitoring line-of-balance and linear programmes

Figure 50 shows the line-of-balance schedule given in Fig. 19, updated to show progress at week 50. This shows that the foundations gradually fell a little behind schedule but not enough to cause problems. Walls started late and are proceeding more slowly than planned, whereas the roofers are working faster than planned and so will soon be brought to a halt by the wall builders. Urgent managerial action is needed to increase the rate of wall production.

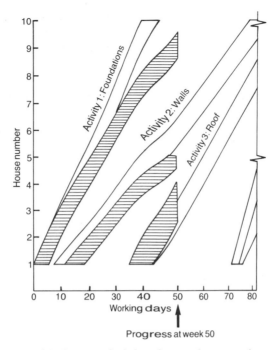

Fig. 50. Line-of-balance schedule for ten-house project: progress at week 50

This simple example shows how effective line-of-balance can be in monitoring and control. Unfortunately, showing progress on a complicated line-of-balance programme can simply result in a mass of incomprehensible lines. To be effective line-of-balance programmes must be kept at a fairly simple level of detail. Linear programmes can be updated in the same way, and the same simplicity is obviously required.

5.13. Management information systems

This guide is about construction planning. In this chapter, the basic concepts have been explained and it has been shown how planning and planning techniques may be used to form the basis of monitoring and control. What has not been described, and is beyond the scope of this guide, is how management information systems are designed and implemented to provide the necessary information. These systems can provide the basis for control of all the resources and costs shown in Table 16, and so they can be complex and therefore need to be explained in more detail than would be appropriate here. Further information can be found in reference 11.

6 Putting planning into practice

This chapter concentrates on the more practical and organizational aspects of planning. To be effective and efficient, planners need a good environment, with adequate space and good sources of information. Planners must make a careful and methodical appraisal of a new project. They have to interact with the other members of the project management team, and so must develop skills of communication and presentation. An example is given of how the plan is developed — shaped — to produce an effective solution, based on an actual project. Construction projects are dynamic and ever-changing, and this powerful influence on planning is analysed.

The preceding chapters covered the elements of the planning process; the early decisions to be made, techniques, resource analysis, monitoring and control procedures. This chapter looks at some of the practical aspects of using these elements to produce working plans. Fig. 51, which follows the planning process from the original brief to the handing-over of the working plan, serves as a guide to the sections in this chapter.

6.1. Working space

The planner's first essential is a working environment free from disturbance. The task of assimilating information from drawings and documents, building the project mentally and then writing down those building instructions is difficult enough without distraction from intrusive telephones and talkative colleagues.

There will of course be those important meetings with others when shaping the plan, but, for the most part, with the exception of short-term programming, detailed planning is essentially a *solo activity*. Therefore the planner's office should be as self-contained

			Section
	Initial appraisal: a general look at the project data	What sort of project? What are the major features, risks and conditions?	6.2
	Early decisions: what sort of plan is needed?	Who is the plan for? What is the level of detail? What timescale?	2.1 2.2 2.3 6.3
	Detailed appraisal: a methodical second look at the project data	What are the constraints? What are the risks?	6.4
	Project team conferences: essential two-way communication	Briefing the team Involving the project manager	6.5
	Planning techniques: appropriate methods of analysis	Bar chart, line-of-balance, linear programme or network?	3.4 3.5 3.6 3.7
	Resource scheduling: men, machines, materials money and time	Aggregation, smoothing, levelling	4
	Shaping: balancing direct costs and site overheads	Could more resources reduce project time and cost?	6.6
	Monitoring: keeping the plan on the rails	Controlling risk Monitoring resource use	5.1 5.4

Fig. 51. The elements of planning and control

as possible with all equipment, documents and reference books easily to hand. Sharing commonly used reference documents is a false economy, because every borrowing sortie is a potential source of distraction for both borrower and lender.

In the early stages of planning the planner will want to keep sight of the general arrangement and site layout drawings while referring to the various detail drawings. It will ease pressure on the precious table space if these general layout drawings can be pinned to the wall. They will be to hand when the planner needs them and available for the conferences and briefing sessions that will be necessary later. Here then are two further essentials of the planner's office: *plenty of table and wall space.*

6.2. Initial appraisal

For most planners a project begins with a pile of documents and a roll of drawings. A planner working in the post-design phase may receive drawings that have been completely detailed with specification and contract documentation complete; planners working in an earlier phase may only receive a few sketches and an oral briefing. Whatever the scale of supply, the initial data need to be appraised twice: screened generally for an initial appraisal, then later assessed in detail to extract the essential project features that must be allowed for in drawing up the plan.

The initial appraisal is to enable the planner to learn just enough about the project to organize the planning period. This appraisal should take only an hour or two and generally will be achieved by seeking the answers to such questions as

- Where is the project and how is it accessed?

- What is the function of the project? How does it work?

- Where are the site boundaries?

- What are the major features and how do they relate to each other?

- What are the principal quantities?

- What are the obvious risks?

- What are the contract conditions?

- How long is the contract period?

For the planner who has to assess many projects it saves time if a standard check-list is prepared incorporating these and other questions; an example is given in Fig. 52.

6.3. Early decisions

The understanding of the project gained by this initial appraisal enables those fundamental decisions discussed in chapters 2 and 3 to be taken. These fundamental decisions are

- Who is the plan for?
- What is the time-scale?
- What is the level of detail?

CONSTRUCTION PLANNING

INITIAL PROJECT APPRAISAL Date 8·1·88 By J C

		ACTION
1. Project title	Factory extension	
2. Client	XYZ Foods plc	
3. Approximate value	£1·5 million	
4. Plan /Tender required at	Place Bristol Date 14·2·88 Time 12·00	
5. Brief description	Single storey portal frame warehouse office accomodation, external works	
6. Conditions of contract	ICE 5th/~~GC Works 1/JCT~~ amended	
7. Method of measurement	~~CESMM2/DTp/SMM6/~~ NA	
8. Standard specification	~~DTp/Water Industry/~~ Own	
9. Covering letter/invitation	Programme + method statements called for	JC
10. Special conditions	Extensive – careful examination required	Sen. QS
11. MM amendments	None	
12. Particular specification	None	
13. BOQ	None. Bills required	Sen. QS
14. Form of tender	Yes	
15. Form/s of bond	Not required	
16. Other documents	Site investigation report	Des. Eng
17. Form of contract	Design + build	
18. Payment terms	Lump sum, priced bills required	
19. Design requirements	Yes	
20. Access	Through existing works. OK	
21. Principal quantities	Factory floor area 1000m² Ext. hardstanding 5000m²	
22. Major features	Portal frame building. Ext. works M + E subcontract	
23. Risks	Nothing unusual. High level of damages. £1000/day	
24. Planning needed	Network-based bar chart /method statements	
25. Planning time estimate	IA½/DA1/Site 1/Plan 2 Total 4½	JC

Fig. 52. Example of a standard initial appraisal check-list

106

- Which planning techniques should be used?

Answering these latter questions, perhaps after referring to Table 2 and Fig. 7, will leave the planner with a very clear idea of the form and content of the plan he must make. For example, a planner working for a management contractor at the start of a commission to design and build a sewage treatment works might decide that

- the plan is for the project manager to enable him to administer and co-ordinate the designers, subcontractors and suppliers

- the time-scale must include not only design and construction but proving, commissioning and maintenance periods, approximately 3 + 12 + 12 = 27 months

- the level of detail needs to be accurate enough to record the arrival and departure of subcontractors and therefore the programme time unit should be weeks rather than months

- the project is complex and will involve many parties, and therefore network analysis is an appropriate planning technique

- because the management contractor intends to pass on much of the risk to subcontractors, the details of labour, plant and materials resources are not a primary concern. There will therefore be no need to carry out resources analysis at this stage of the planning.

Table 17. *Time allowed for planning the example project*

Activity	Time allowed: days
Detailed appraisal of feasibility study	0·5
Research a similar project completed last year for another client	0·5
Draw up a network	1
Time activities and input network data onto computer	1
Print bar chart as output, check results and draft short covering report	0·5
Total	3·5

To continue with the example, when the planner has made these early decisions, he is then able to assess how much time should be allowed for the planning. As the project is at an early stage and the only prime document is a consultant's feasibility study, the planner draws conclusions which are given in Table 17. With a clear idea of the task to be undertaken and the time required to do it, the planner can move on to the detailed appraisal.

6.4. Detailed appraisal

Whereas the initial appraisal may be dealt with quickly by a cursory examination of the drawings and documents, the detailed appraisal needs to be undertaken methodically and carefully, and, most importantly, *only once*. A project brief may contain any or all of the main documents listed in Table 18 as well as references to a number of secondary documents.

Reading documents efficiently requires method. What is the reader looking for? The answers are

● generally

○ any instruction or specification departing from the accepted normal standard (as laid down in the secondary documents)

● specifically

*Table 18. Main and secondary tender documents**

Main documents	Secondary documents
Covering letter/invitation to tender	
Special conditions	Conditions of contract
Particular conditions of contract	
Amendments to method of measurement	Standard method of measurement
Preamble to the bills of quantities	
Bills of quantities	
Particular specifications	Standard specification
	British Standard specifications
Site investigation report	
Programme	
Drawings	Standard details
Form of tender	Background drawings available for
Form(s) of bond	inspection at client's offices

*A set of tender documents may not include any of the secondary documents listed here. The planner will need to have a set available and be familiar with the contents.

o   any instructions concerning possession of the site or restriction of accesses
o   any other instructions affecting the planner's freedom to plan the works
o   any design rules affecting construction, for example, speed of placing filling material, minimum age for loading concrete structures.

To ensure that this detailed (and often tedious) appraisal is only carried out once, referenced notes must be made. When these notes are attached to the preliminary appraisal checklist, they provide a distillation of all the main issues affecting the plan; their importance cannot be overstated.

If the documents under appraisal are planner's copies which do not have to be returned to the client, reference numbers may be marked in ink directly on to the margin of the document. If this is not possible a light pencil number in the margin and/or a paper flag stuck to the page may act as markers. Each note should precis the point made in the document and echo the questions raised in the planner's mind when he read the original text, as shown in Table 19.

As this appraisal will be read by a number of other people in the project team who may wish to refer back to the source documents for clarification, the importance of a clear reference system is obvious.

Table 19. Example of planner's notes on a detailed appraisal

Reference	Page	Item	Comment
42	15	Specification calls for beam soffit shutters to remain for 14 days after casting concrete.	This could hinder progress. Enquire client's reasoning. Can this period be shortened?
43	17	On-site batching is specified.	Estimator to make allowance for setting up batcher, or qualify tender for ready-mixed concrete supply.

6.5. Planning and conferring

After the detailed appraisal the planner may begin to plan. All is to hand: the layout drawings are on display; the detailed drawings are piled in order; the appraisal notes are complete; the office is peaceful and telephone calls have been diverted.

The process of building up the plan will entail a number of conferences with colleagues. The first of these may take place after the detailed appraisal. This is an appropriate time for the planner, who by now has a good knowledge of the project, to brief the remainder of the project team, who will at this stage know little or nothing about the project. Such a briefing, together with a set of appraisal notes, will undoubtedly save the other members of the team many hours of reading.

At this point the project manager must begin to participate actively in the planning process. He should work with the planner to establish the broad strategy of the plan, complementing the planner's detailed knowledge with his own broad experience of construction and his knowledge of company resources and policy. The project manager might comment on site conditions, e.g.

- there were serious groundwater problems in this area 10 years ago. Arrange for some additional trial pits.

or use of resources, e.g.

- a batching plant will become available shortly; check if the concreting operations can be programmed close together to make site batching economic

or perhaps on risk

- this project is beyond the company's experience and fraught with potential problems. The company should not tender for it.

Near the end of the planning process a further conference may be called to brief the project team and collect their comments, criticism and advice. Such conferences require the planner to master a few presentation skills if ideas are to be put over clearly and thereby claim the attention (and co-operation) of colleagues. The secret of successful presentation, as in concreting, or any other process, lies in careful preparation.

- Separate the drawings and charts needed and place them in the order of display.

- Colour areas of drawings which need to be referred to.

- Have suitable wall or table space available to display drawings.

- On one side of A4 paper list the main headings of the presentation in a logical order, for example

  o introduction: project history and purpose
  o location and access
  o project description
  o outline programme and methods
  o resources
  o summary of problems.

Usually the planner will be so familiar with the project that he will be able to speak quite fluently without notes, requiring only the list of main headings and the plans as reference documents.

Planning conferences need to be carefully minuted; problems identified, decisions made and actions called for must be carefully listed. It is good practice to circulate these minutes promptly to all those involved as a reminder to take any actions called for.

6.6. Shaping the plan

Although at the outset there may appear to be many ways of building the project, the planner's careful appraisals, consultations and deliberations will eventually narrow the options to a single, reasonably robust plan of construction. The project activities may then be resourced and this plan tested to see if it meets the requirements of project time and imposed resource levels. If the plan survives those tests, it will then require shaping to ensure that the resource levels provide the most economic construction cost.

Shaping is balancing direct costs against site overhead costs to give a minimum construction cost; it is the operation that contractors carry out when refining their tenders and it usually has to be done on a trial-and-error basis. Fortunately, there is now network-based computer software available which enables any number of trial-and-error solutions to be carried out quickly and relatively painlessly.

Shaping is done by drawing a cost-resourced network to accommodate not only the direct costs but also the time-related indirect (or overhead) costs as hammock activities. Examples of time-related overhead costs are: maintaining site offices and workshops; site supervision; general site plant. Sometimes major plant items such as a tower crane, cofferdam, central batching plant, floodlighting, scaffolding or a generator are also time-related overhead costs. There may be also finance and management charges levied on a time-related basis.

Figure 53 illustrates an accommodation bridge to be constructed to carry a minor road across a new dual carriageway road. The bridge is to be built under a separate contract from the main road works and the client has stipulated that the bridge contractor shall provide a full time agent on site. The contractor's project manager believes a full time agent for such a modest structure to be an unduly burdensome overhead and asks the planner to take the site overheads into account and programme to achieve least cost.

The planner, intending to use a computer program to find the least cost solution, depicts the project in the form of a precedence network (Fig. 54). He first links the activities by logic restraints assuming infinite resources to be available and then adds the resource restraints (broken lines) using the following reasoning.

- One excavation team will excavate the four foundations in turn (restraints 210−310, 310−410, 410−510).

- Only one set of bankseat forms will be made (restraint 420−520).

- Only one set of pier forms will be made (restraint 230−330).

The next stage requires input from the estimator. The direct costs of construction activities are entered into the activity boxes and the site overheads added as hammock activities. Each hammock restraint is positioned carefully to show the start and finish of the

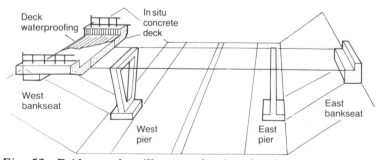

Fig. 53. Bridge used to illustrate shaping the plan

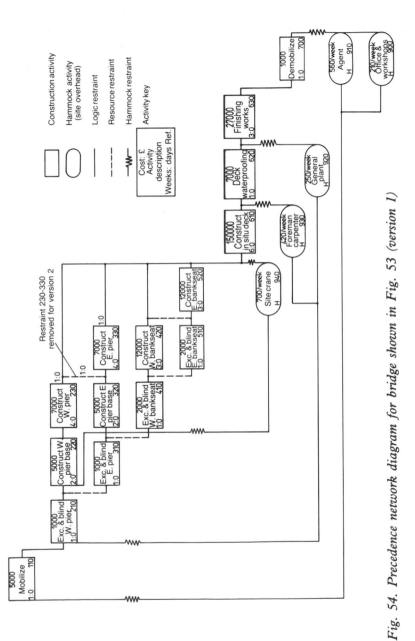

Fig. 54. Precedence network diagram for bridge shown in Fig. 53 (version 1)

particular overhead charge. For example, the agent, who costs £560 per week is shown for the total project time whereas the foreman carpenter, costing £420, is charged from the start of the pier excavation only until completion of the in situ deck (activities 210—610).

Care must be taken in choosing the positions of hammock restraints to ensure that the network logic will not be upset should resource restraints be altered later.

Once the resourced network has been completed, the planner now enters the data into the computer. The results, in the form of bar chart and cumulative cost histogram, are shown in Figs 55 and 56. The planner notes the following.

- First version

o the project time is 24 weeks
o the total cost £283 640
o the critical path goes through pier construction activities.

As the object of this exercise is to attempt to achieve an overall saving by shortening the construction period, the planner examines the critical path to see if additional resources can be applied to any critical activities. He decides that activities 230 and 330, construction of the piers, could be carried out simultaneously and alters the network by removing restraint 230—330. He reasons that the cost of an additional set of pier forms might be more than offset by the savings in overheads. The estimator advises that an extra set of pier forms will cost £3000 so the planner amends the resource costs by spreading this extra cost equally over activities 230 and 330.

The data held on the computer are amended and a new programme and cumulative cost histogram produced, as shown in Figs 57 and 58, summarized as follows

- Second version

o the project time is 20 weeks
o the total cost £278 080
o the critical path goes through both pier and bankseat activities.

The comparison with the first version shows that the shortened programme offers a 16% time saving and a 2% cost saving; enough to win a tender or double a profit margin! Fig. 59 shows a graphical comparison of the cumulative cost.

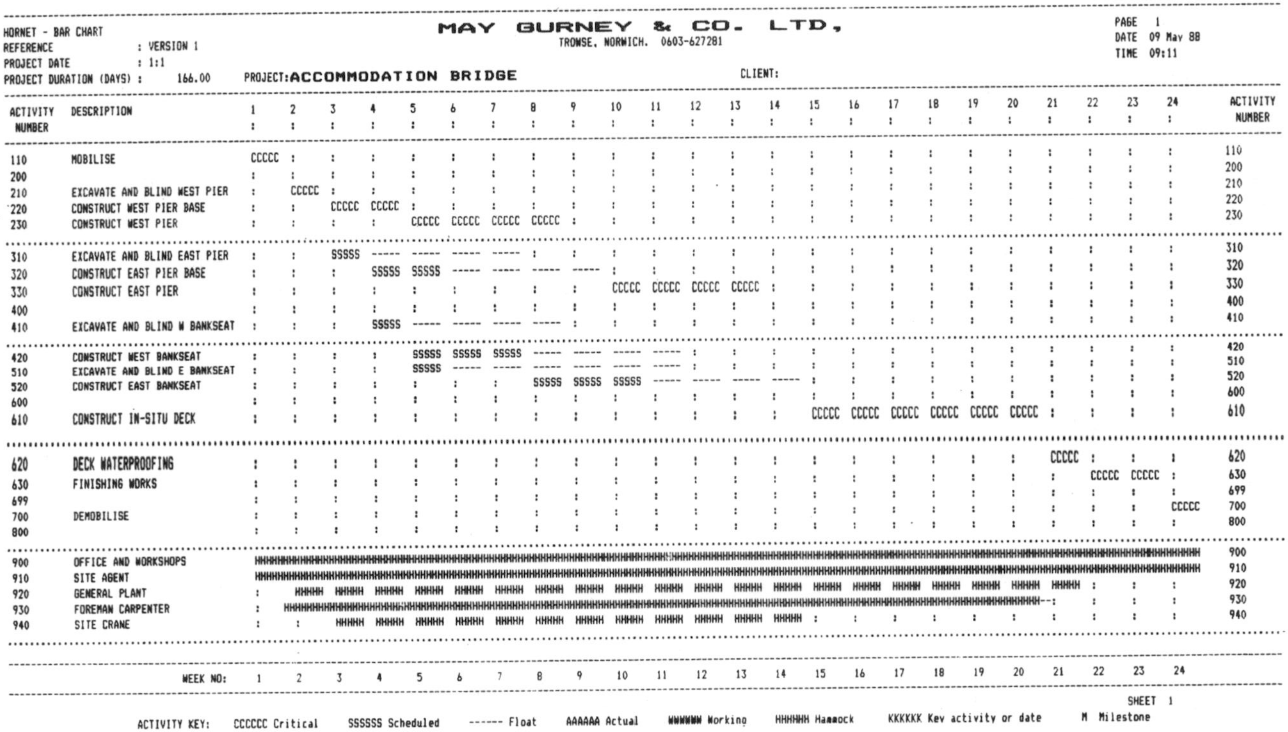

HORNET - BAR CHART
REFERENCE   : VERSION 1
PROJECT DATE   : 1:1
PROJECT DURATION (DAYS) :   166.00

MAY GURNEY & CO. LTD,
TROWSE, NORWICH.   0603-627281

PAGE 1
DATE 09 May 88
TIME 09:11

PROJECT: ACCOMMODATION BRIDGE   CLIENT:

ACTIVITY NUMBER	DESCRIPTION	1	2	3	4	5	6	7	8	9	10	11	12	13	14	15	16	17	18	19	20	21	22	23	24	ACTIVITY NUMBER
110	MOBILISE	CCCCC																								110
200																										200
210	EXCAVATE AND BLIND WEST PIER		CCCCC																							210
220	CONSTRUCT WEST PIER BASE			CCCCC	CCCCC																					220
230	CONSTRUCT WEST PIER					CCCCC	CCCCC	CCCCC	CCCCC																	230
310	EXCAVATE AND BLIND EAST PIER			SSSSS	-----	-----	-----	-----	-----																	310
320	CONSTRUCT EAST PIER BASE				SSSSS	SSSSS	-----	-----	-----	-----																320
330	CONSTRUCT EAST PIER										CCCCC	CCCCC	CCCCC	CCCCC												330
400																										400
410	EXCAVATE AND BLIND W BANKSEAT				SSSSS	-----	-----																			410
420	CONSTRUCT WEST BANKSEAT						SSSSS	SSSSS	SSSSS	-----	-----	-----	-----													420
510	EXCAVATE AND BLIND E BANKSEAT					SSSSS	-----	-----																		510
520	CONSTRUCT EAST BANKSEAT								SSSSS	SSSSS	SSSSS	-----	-----	-----												520
600																										600
610	CONSTRUCT IN-SITU DECK														CCCCC	CCCCC	CCCCC	CCCCC	CCCCC	CCCCC						610
620	DECK WATERPROOFING																					CCCCC				620
630	FINISHING WORKS																						CCCCC	CCCCC		630
699																										699
700	DEMOBILISE																								CCCCC	700
800																										800
900	OFFICE AND WORKSHOPS	HHHHHHHHHHHHHHHHHHHHHHHHHHHHHHHHHHHHHHHHHHHHHHHHHHHHHHHHHHHHHHHHHHHHHHHHHHHHHHHHHHHHHHHHHHHHHHHHHHHHHHHHHHHHHHHHHHHHHHHHHHHHHH																								900
910	SITE AGENT	HHHHHHHHHHHHHHHHHHHHHHHHHHHHHHHHHHHHHHHHHHHHHHHHHHHHHHHHHHHHHHHHHHHHHHHHHHHHHHHHHHHHHHHHHHHHHHHHHHHHHHHHHHHHHHHHHHHHHHHHHHHHHH																								910
920	GENERAL PLANT		HHHHH	HHHHH	HHHHH	HHHHH	HHHHH	HHHHH	HHHHH	HHHHH	HHHHH	HHHHH	HHHHH	HHHHH	HHHHH	HHHHH	HHHHH	HHHHH	HHHHH	HHHHH	HHHHH	HHHHH--:				920
930	FOREMAN CARPENTER		HHHHHHHHHHHHHHHHHHHHHHHHHHHHHHHHHHHHHHHHHHHHHHHHHHHHHHHHHHHHHHHHHHH								HHHHH														930
940	SITE CRANE			HHHHH	HHHHH	HHHHH	HHHHH	HHHHH	HHHHH	HHHHH	HHHHH	HHHHH	HHHHH	HHHHH												940

WEEK NO:	1	2	3	4	5	6	7	8	9	10	11	12	13	14	15	16	17	18	19	20	21	22	23	24

ACTIVITY KEY: CCCCC Critical   SSSSS Scheduled   ------ Float   AAAAA Actual   WWWWW Working   HHHHH Hammock   KKKKK Key activity or date   M Milestone

SHEET 1

PRACTICE

115

Fig. 55. Bar chart for first version of bridge

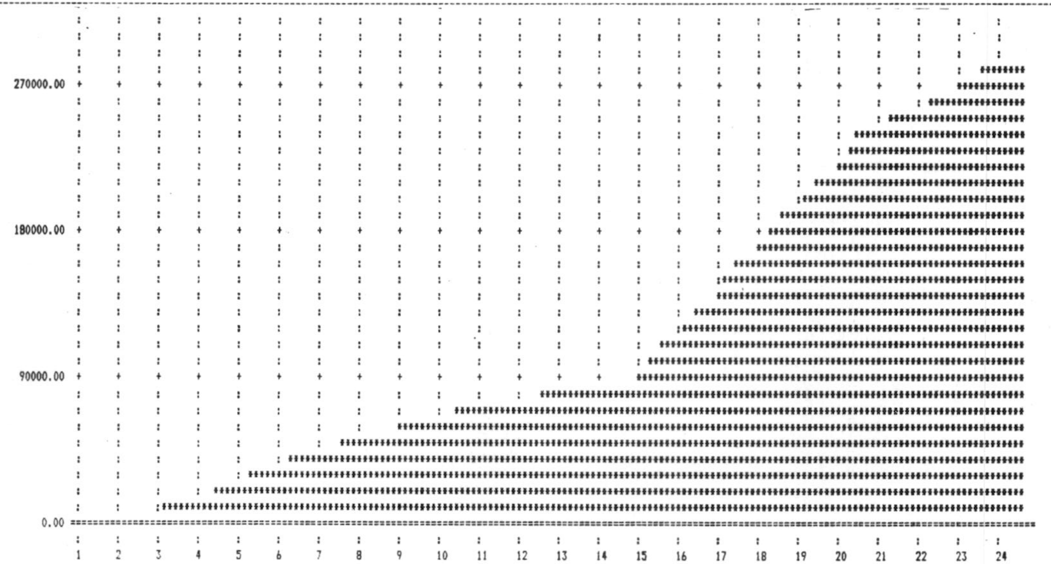

Fig. 56. Histogram for first version of bridge showing total cumulative cost

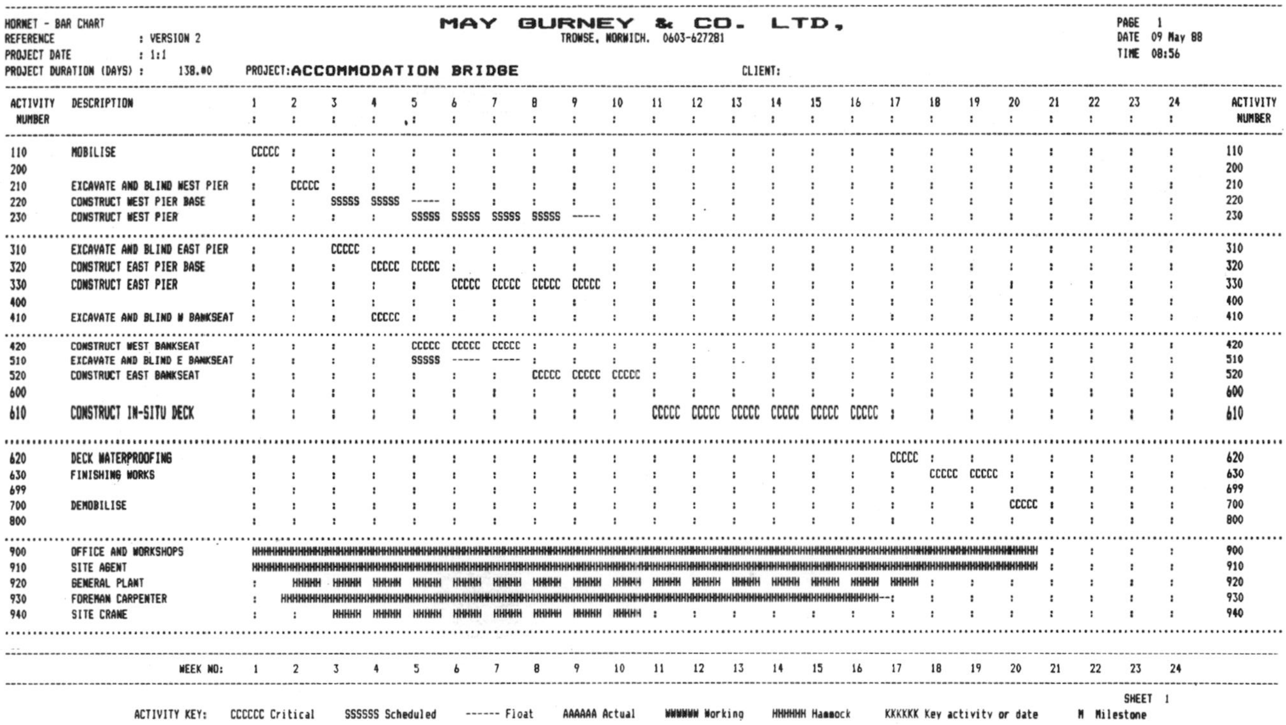

HORNET - BAR CHART   : VERSION 2
REFERENCE
PROJECT DATE   : 1:1
PROJECT DURATION (DAYS) : 138.00   PROJECT:ACCOMMODATION BRIDGE   CLIENT:

MAY GURNEY & CO. LTD.
TROWSE, NORWICH. 0603-627781

PAGE 1
DATE 09 May 88
TIME 08:56

ACTIVITY NUMBER	DESCRIPTION	ACTIVITY NUMBER
110	MOBILISE	110
200		200
210	EXCAVATE AND BLIND WEST PIER	210
220	CONSTRUCT WEST PIER BASE	220
230	CONSTRUCT WEST PIER	230
310	EXCAVATE AND BLIND EAST PIER	310
320	CONSTRUCT EAST PIER BASE	320
330	CONSTRUCT EAST PIER	330
400		400
410	EXCAVATE AND BLIND W BANKSEAT	410
420	CONSTRUCT WEST BANKSEAT	420
510	EXCAVATE AND BLIND E BANKSEAT	510
520	CONSTRUCT EAST BANKSEAT	520
600		600
610	CONSTRUCT IN-SITU DECK	610
620	DECK WATERPROOFING	620
630	FINISHING WORKS	630
699		699
700	DEMOBILISE	700
800		800
900	OFFICE AND WORKSHOPS	900
910	SITE AGENT	910
920	GENERAL PLANT	920
930	FOREMAN CARPENTER	930
940	SITE CRANE	940

WEEK NO: 1 2 3 4 5 6 7 8 9 10 11 12 13 14 15 16 17 18 19 20 21 22 23 24

ACTIVITY KEY: CCCCC Critical   SSSSS Scheduled   AAAAA Actual   ------ Float   WWWWW Working   HHHHH Hammock   KKKKK Key activity or date   M Milestone

SHEET 1

Fig. 57. Bar chart for second version of bridge

117

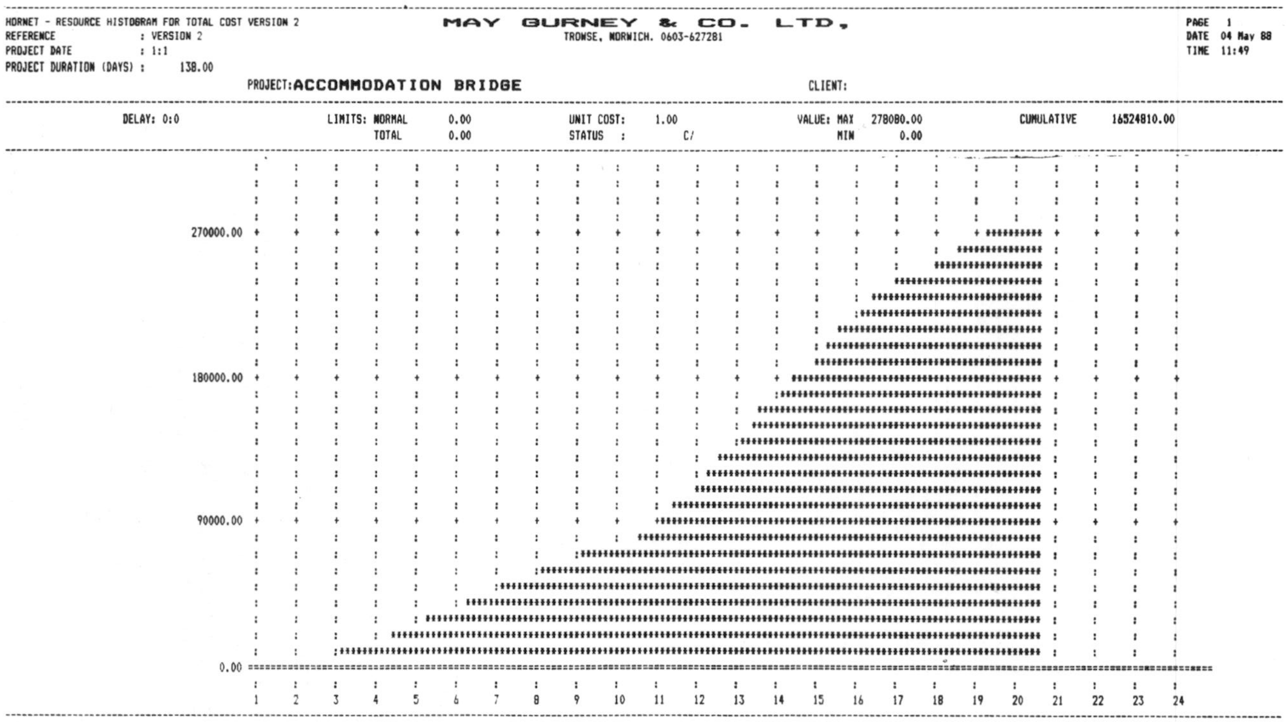

Fig. 58. Histogram for second version of bridge showing total cumulative cost

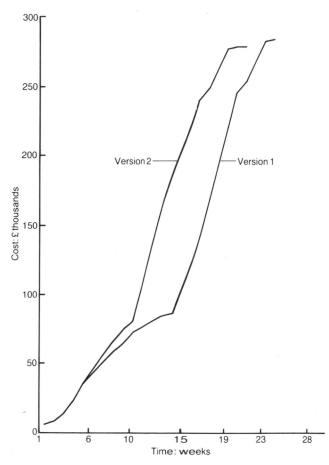

Fig. 59. Comparison of costs of versions 1 and 2

6.7. Variations and project control

Computer-based network analysis programmes may be used not only as a rapid means of shaping the plan by evaluating alternatives, but also for predicting the effect of variations on the progress of a project. If a fully resourced network is maintained on disc in a site-based microcomputer the effects of changes to the programme may be known at once.

One of the most common ways in which a contract may be varied, albeit usually an unintentional one, is by the late provision of information from the client to the contractor. The client may be unaware of the disastrous effect the delay will have on progress until months later when presented with a claim for disruption.

How much better that the planner should use his skills to estimate the cost of the disruption and thereby motivate the client to provide the information earlier and avoid the resultant dispute? With a resourced network programme it is only necessary to reprogramme the one activity affected by the late supply of information and then ask the computer to produce a cumulative cost evaluation. The results could be dramatic

Dear Sir

You will note from the attached print-out that we estimate that the cost of the delay caused by waiting for the bending schedules may amount to £10 000 per week.

Systems of this type, which enable the planner to construct a model of the project and store it in the computer, are immensely useful for project control but do demand a high degree of devotion from the planner. To enable the computer to make a rapid response to changes, the project model must be completely up-to-date. On large sites, with a resident planner dedicated to the task, impressive results may be achieved. On most other sites the crises of the day will usually take preference to updating the network with the result that it will never be available to respond to immediate demands.

6.8. Handing over the plan, the narrative report

Reference to Fig. 3 will remind the reader that a plan may need to be communicated by a number of output documents. The professional planner will want to hand these documents over as a package accompanied by a cover note listing the contents. Although the Authors have yet to hear of a planner being sued for negligence, the planner runs the same risk as any other construction professional who sells a service. It is therefore prudent to ensure that all planning documents are accounted and signed for. In that way it should be possible to avoid ordering materials from out of date resource lists or scheduling supplies from superseded programmes.

One output document which has not been mentioned so far in this guide is the narrative report. This is an important document to be used on those occasions when it is impossible for the planner to present his plan to those who will implement it. This document is a useful means of putting a plan into context; it should contain

- a brief summary of the planning philosophy

- mention of any misgivings or reservations the planner may have about his plan

- any recommendations for further action, i.e. updating, monitoring, resourcing, etc.

Whenever possible the opportunity should be taken to allow the planner to present his plan to the project team. The value of this presentation lies not only in the time saved by the project team in their comprehension of the project, but also by impressing on the planner that his plans are not a theoretical exercise but are implemented by real people.

6.9. The dynamics of project management

One of the major differences between the management of construction projects and the management of a manufacturing process is the continual change and development that occurs through the life of a project, making the manager's task very demanding. Imagine, for example, the process of constructing a large building. The initial stages may require the management of heavy civil engineering work in the excavation and construction of the basement. Such work is subject to the effects of weather and ground condition, uses heavy plant and is constructed to quite large tolerances by a robust set of people. The project will then progress through work of increasing refinement: structural frame, enclosure, services, etc., finishing with the exacting work of telecommunications and high quality finishes.

This changing and developing nature of projects means that planning has to be done for organization changes as well as for the physical work. The project organization will change, and the people in it, as — to continue with the building example — those people with expertise in groundworks are replaced by those who know about the technology of building and the management of building trades contractors. This progression of organization must be planned in advance because it sets the *context* and *structure* of the work plan. That is, this organizational development will determine the way in which the master plan is broken down into detailed plans, and this in turn will set up the structure of the system for monitoring and control.

6.10. The changing emphasis of planning

In the initial stages of planning, the emphasis is on the method of construction and the estimation and scheduling of the resources that will be required. Management's concentration is on the achievement of deadlines and the efficient procurement of resources. By contrast, in the middle of the project, the plan has been made, the resources have arrived and management becomes more concerned with the day-to-day efficiency of the use of resources; perhaps to the extent of neglecting to concentrate equally on the timely achievement of project objectives.

Expressed more simply, this is a change from 'how many pipe-laying gangs will be needed?' to 'what are we going to do with Charlie's gang next week?' It is likely that to keep Charlie's gang productively occupied, the project manager may change the method and sequence of construction, if this is possible, rather than have the gang standing idle. Thus in the middle of the project the *emphasis changes* such that current planning thought is no longer dominated by *construction method*, but by *resource utilization*. This has a quite profound effect on the planning, and of course means that the nature of the master plan may be substantially different from that of the weekly section plan. The danger is that this concentration on resource utilization may result in late completion of the project.

6.11. Short-term planning

Table 2 made reference to weekly or two-weekly plans for foremen, gangers and trade foremen. Such short-term programmes need to be compiled in a different way from long-term strategic programmes. The rule that planning should be carried out single-handed by a planner working on his own without interruption does not apply here.

Short-term programmes are about the use of specific named resources. They describe what individual gangs and items of plant should achieve in half day periods. To be successful these programmes must be compiled by, or with, the general foreman or work supervisor. Whoever does the plotting, the foreman must have a full say in the disposition of his resources. To present a foreman with a short-term works programme without consultation would be setting up a challenge which the planner could not win. A typical short-term works programme is shown in Fig. 60.

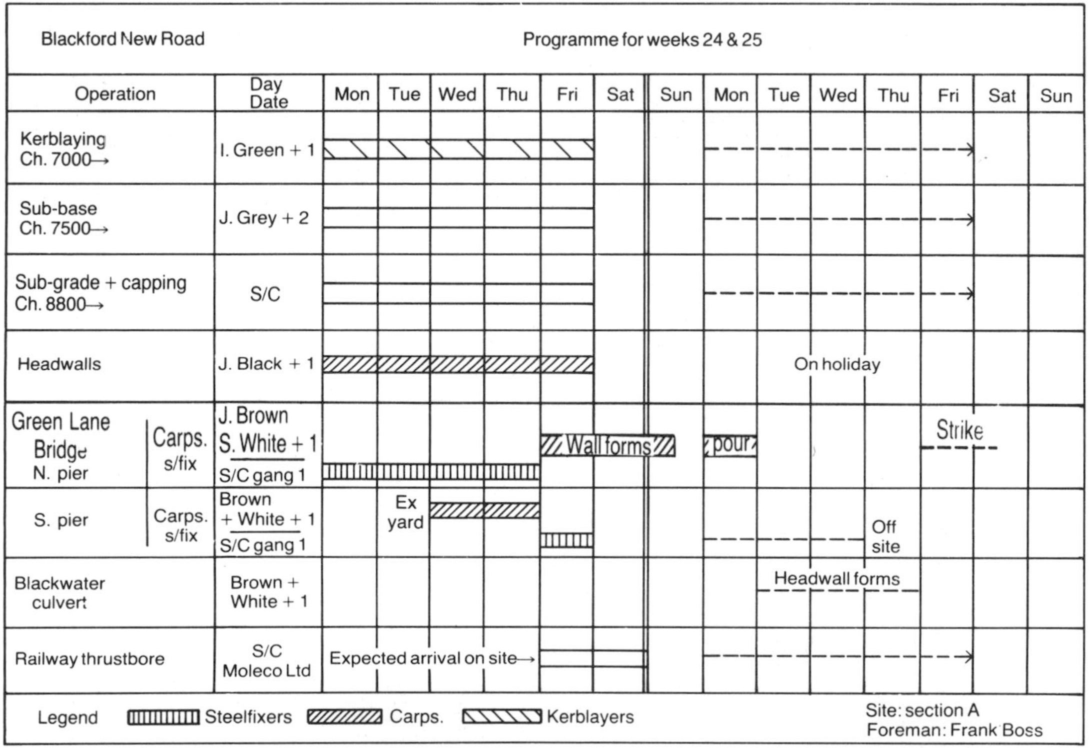

Fig. 60. Example of a short-term plan

6.12. Summary

This guide has given a brief but comprehensive review of the whole process of construction planning. The emphasis has been laid on the organizational and procedural aspects of planning, illustrating the complex context in which the construction planner has to work. There is, clearly, much more to construction planning than the mastery of planning techniques and computer systems, although such mastery — and fluent skill — is absolutely vital. Thus careful preparatory work, building a sound technical, procedural and organizational strategy, is the essential prerequisite for successful construction planning and control. In the case studies given in chapter 7, all of which are taken from actual projects, some indication of the broader context within which the plan was shaped has been given, as well as examples of the practical application of each of the four principal planning techniques.

7 Case studies

This chapter comprises three case studies, all derived from actual construction projects. The case studies are: a line-of-balance programme for a low-cost housing project in a developing country; a linear programme (time-chainage chart) for a dual carriageway trunk road and structures in the UK; and network analysis, in precedence form, applied to a raw water pumping station and storage lagoons, in the UK.

7.1. Line-of-balance case study

Project: Low-cost housing
Title: Bukit Nusa Indah Estate, Jakarta, Indonesia
Client: P.T. Nusa May Gurney
Planning brief: Short-term planning for resource utilization

Description

The plan is for one group of 130 houses within a much larger project (Fig. 61). The requirements of the project indicate that these houses must be constructed as fast as possible. Fig. 62 shows the design of the houses, all of which are identical. The purpose of this case study is to illustrate the use of the line-of-balance planning technique. The description is structured along the lines of the anatomy of planning techniques given in section 3.1.

Activities

Houses are constructed by groups of tradesmen having well-defined skills. Thus the trade activities become the basis for planning and control. Table 20 lists the activities for each housing unit, illustrating a sensible level of detail for planning such a project.

Fig. 61. Low-cost housing, first case study

Activity durations
The duration of each activity for each housing unit is derived from the estimate of the man-hours required. This is given in the man-hours per unit, column M.

Project time-scale
Some estimate has to be made of the necessary hand-over rate, to establish a common rate of work for all trades. Obviously this would be easy if the client had specified a hand-over rate, but in this case only the overall project time-scale has been given: 6 months (26 weeks or 182 days).

Work method
The principal factors to be considered are

- the staff and other overhead costs of the UK contractor are high, so a time-scale shorter than 6 months would bring significant financial savings

- the uncertainties associated with working in a developing country indicate that it would be prudent to include a safety period between the contractor's planned completion date and the client's required date.

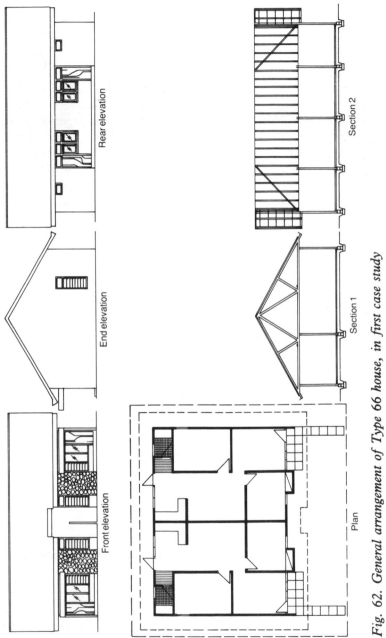

Rear elevation

End elevation

Front elevation

Section 2

Section 1

Plan

Fig. 62. General arrangement of Type 66 house, in first case study

127

Thus the planner must answer two major related questions

- what should be the planned completion date of the work?
- what should be the planned weekly output of housing units?

The problem is an illustration of the statement made in section 1.6 which emphasizes the need for skilled and experienced planners, because it can only be solved by a combination of experience, and trial and error. After some preliminary calculations, and discussion with the senior managers, the planner decides to make a first analysis on the assumptions of a working rate of 24 houses per week, which he believed to be the practical maximum rate, and a working week of 60 hours. The calculations are set out in the form of a schedule, in Table 20; these calculations are explained briefly here.

Column M, man-hours per house, is derived from estimates made by the local contractor.

Column N, theoretical number of men required, is derived from the number of man-hours per housing unit, and the number of units required per week (24), divided by the number of working

Table 20. Basic duration calculations for line-of-balance case study: see text for explanation of quantities

Activity number and description	M: man-h per unit	N	n	A	H	R	t: days	T: days	B: days
1. Foundation	127	50·8	6	54	9	25·5	2·1	30·3	1
2. Well	140	56	7	56	8	24·0	2·0	32·3	1
3. Plumber 1	79	31·6	4	32	8	24·3	2·0	31·8	3
4. Blockwork 1	439	175·6	12	180	15	24·6	3·7	31·5	5
5. Roofing 1	438	175·2	6	180	30	24·7	7·3	31·4	5
6. Electrician 1	28	11·2	2	12	6	25·7	1·4	30·1	1
7. Plumber 2	2	0·8	1	1	1	30·0	0·2	25·8	1
8. Rendering	651	260·4	18	270	15	24·9	3·6	31·1	4
9. Roofing 2	99	39·6	4	40	10	24·2	2·5	31·9	1
10. Flooring	130	52	8	56	7	25·8	1·6	29·9	3
11. Plumber 3	12	4·8	1	5	5	25·0	1·2	31·0	1
12. Carpenter and glazier	123	49·2	6	54	9	26·3	2·1	29·4	1
13. Electrician 2	54	21·6	2	22	11	24·4	2·7	31·7	3
14. Ext. works	465	186	8	192	24	24·8	5·8	31·2	
15. Painter	730	312	10	320	32	24·6	7·8	31·4	

hours in a week, in this case 60, assuming a six-day week of ten hours per day.

Column n, men per house, is a practical estimate of the number of men required to complete each activity for one housing unit. This is based on a knowledge of the normal grouping of men in each trade (for example plumbers usually work in pairs and two masons usually work with one labourer) adjusted as necessary to achieve the necessary total output. This figure is determined by the planner and senior managers.

Column A, actual number of men, is the theoretical value N corrected by the introduction of the practical estimate of the number of men per house n. Thus, for activity 1, N is $50 \cdot 8$; so for $n = 6$, realistic values of A are either $6 \times 8 = 48$ (i.e. eight groups of six men) or $6 \times 9 = 54$ (nine groups of six men). In this case, the planner has chosen the faster rate, so activity 1 will proceed at a rate slightly faster than the general rate of 24 houses per week.

Column H, the number of houses worked on simultaneously, is part of the calculation for column A; e.g. nine groups of six men, giving $A = 54$, means also that these nine groups will work on one house each.

Column R, the actual rate of house production per week, is the calculation for the adjusted, practical number of men to be used; e.g. for activity 1, the theoretical number of men is $50 \cdot 8$, but the realistic plan is to use nine groups of six men, i.e. 54 men. Thus the planned rate of house production per week will be increased by the factor $54 \div 50 \cdot 8$. Thus activity 1 is planned to proceed at $25 \cdot 5$ houses per week, not the notional 24.

Column t, the time required for each trade to complete its work on one housing unit, is simply calculated from the man-hours per house divided by the man-hours available per day. Thus activity 1 requires 127 man-hours per house, so a group of six men will take $127/(6 \times 10) = 2 \cdot 1$ days.

Column T is the time required from the start of the first house to the start of the last house. This calculation is necessary to determine the slope of the lines-of-balance for each activity. The slope is the number of housing units, less one, divided by the rate per week R expressed in days. Note that the values of T for each activity should be similar.

Column B is the minimum buffer time, based on a series of decisions made by the planner and project manager. Note that the major

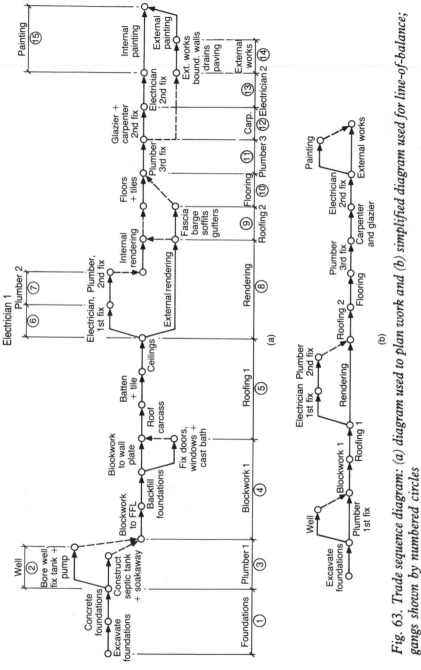

Fig. 63. Trade sequence diagram: (a) diagram used to plan work and (b) simplified diagram used for line-of-balance; gangs shown by numbered circles

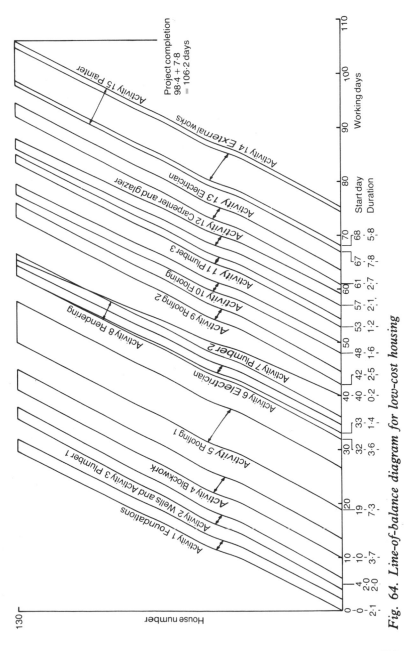

Fig. 64. Line-of-balance diagram for low-cost housing

131

Table 21. Calculations for drawing line-of-balance diagram

Activity number and description	Time for one unit: days	Elapsed time: days	Buffer: days	Start day calculation unit 1	Start day calculation unit 130
1. Foundations	2·1	30·3	1	Project start　　0	$0+30\cdot3 \longrightarrow 30\cdot3$
2. Well	2·0	32·3	1	$0+2\cdot1+1=3\cdot1 \longrightarrow 4$ Follows 1, slower	$4+32\cdot3 \longrightarrow 36\cdot3$
3. Plumber 1	2·0	31·8	3	$0+2\cdot1+1=3\cdot1 \longrightarrow 4$ Follows 1, slower	$4+31\cdot8 \longrightarrow 35\cdot8$
4. Blockwork 1	3·7	31·5	5	$40\cdot8-31\cdot5=9\cdot3 \longrightarrow 10$ Follows 2 & 3, faster than both	$10+31\cdot5 \longrightarrow 41\cdot5$ $36\cdot3+2+1=39\cdot3,$ $35\cdot8+2+3=40\cdot8$ therefore follows activity 3
5. Roofing 1	7·3	31·4	5	$50\cdot2-31\cdot4=18\cdot8 \longrightarrow 19$	$19+31\cdot4 \longrightarrow 50\cdot4$ $41\cdot5+3\cdot7+5=50\cdot2$
6. Electrician 1	1·4	30·1	1	$62\cdot7-30\cdot1=32\cdot6 \longrightarrow 33$	$33+30\cdot1 \longrightarrow 63\cdot1$ $50\cdot4+7\cdot3+5=62\cdot7$

7. Plumber 2	0·2	25·8	1	$65·5 - 25·8 = 39·7$ → 40	$40 + 25·8$ → $65·8$ $63·1 + 1·4 + 1 = 65·5$
8. Rendering	3·6	31·1	4	$62·7 - 31·1 = 31·6$ → 32	$32 + 31·1$ → $63·1$ $50·4 + 7·3 + 5 = 62·7$
9. Roofing 2	2·5	31·9	1	$40 + 0·2 + 1 = 41·2$ → 42 Follows 7 & 8, slower than both $32 + 3·6 + 4 = 39·6$	$42 + 31·9$ → $73·9$
10. Flooring	1·6	29·9	3	$77·4 - 29·9 = 47·5$ → 48	$48 + 29·9$ → $77·9$ $73·9 + 2·5 + 1 = 77·4$
11. Plumber 3	1·2	31·0	1	$48 + 1·6 + 3 = 52·6$ → 53	$53 + 31$ → 84
12. Carpenter/glazier	2·1	29·4	1	$86·2 - 29·4 = 56·8$ → 57	$57 + 29·4$ → $86·4$ $84 + 1·2 + 1 = 86·2$
13. Electrician 2	2·7	31·7	3	$57 + 2·1 + 1 = 60·1$ → 61	$61 + 31·7$ → $92·7$
14. External works	5·8	31·2		$98·4 - 31·2 = 67·2$ → 68	$68 + 31·2$ → $99·2$ $92·7 + 2·7 + 3 = 98·4$
15. Painter	7·8	31·4		$98·4 - 31·4 = 67·0$ → 67	$67 + 31·4$ → $98·4$ $92·7 + 2·7 + 3 = 98·4$

133

activities have longer buffers, a commonsense assumption; the completion of the electrical installation is also considered to be rather uncertain.

Construction sequence

The construction sequence is given in Fig. 63, the trade sequence diagram. The actual diagram used to plan the construction is given, and also a simplified diagram used as the basis for the line-of-balance planning.

Drawing the line-of-balance diagram

The line-of-balance diagram is given in Fig. 64, based on the calculations given in Table 21. Care must be taken when calculating the values when activities run in parallel; it is helpful to remember that the buffers are all estimated with reference to the *preceding* activity, i.e. they are an estimate of potential delay of that particular activity. Some notes for guidance on the parallel activities are as follows.

- Activities 2 (well) and 3 (plumber 1) both follow activity 1 (foundations) after a buffer of one day.

- Activity 4 (blockwork 1) follows both activities 2 and 3, so it starts after the latest time of either, i.e. the worst case must be calculated, considering the buffers following both activities 2 and 3.

- Activities 6 (electrician 1) and 8 (rendering) both follow activity 5 (roofing 1) with the roofing buffer of 5 days; activity 7 (plumber 2) follows activity 6 (electrician 1); again the worst case must be calculated. This is an interesting case, because although there is float on activity 7 in each housing unit, the high rate of working means that this is the critical activity, determining the start of activity 9 (roofing 2).

- Activities 14 (external works) and 15 (painting) both follow activity 13 (electrician 2) with a buffer of three days.

The start time of each trade will be an integer. It is unusual for tradesmen to start work on a new project at any other time than at the start of a day; therefore these have been rounded up to the beginning of the following day.

Interpretation

The project ends with two concurrent activities, numbers 14 (external works) and 15 (painter). The estimated project completion date is therefore the latest of

number 14: 99·2 + 5·8 = 105 days or
number 15: 98·4 + 7·8 = 106 · 2 days

for a six-day week, giving a planned project duration of about 18 weeks. This is well inside the target time of 26 weeks.

7.2. Linear programme (time-chainage chart) case study

Project: Dual carriageway trunk road and structures
Title: All Wymondham — Cringleford Improvement
Client: Director (Transport), Department of Transport and Environment
Consulting engineers: G. Maunsell & Partners
Planning brief: Contractor's working plan

Description

In essence the project is 7 km of new dual 9·3 m carriageway trunk road with roundabouts at each end to accommodate connections to the existing road. There are three major structures: a road overpass, a stream underpass and a side road railway bridge. Other features include a staggered junction and 3 km of side roads. The entire project is located on agricultural land and woodland.

Planner's initial appraisal

The initial appraisal is summarized as follows

● The project is located near the contractor's head office and is accessible at both ends and two intermediate points.

● Major features
o 400 000 m³ excavation/filling
o 54 000 m³ imported capping material
o one single carriageway in situ concrete overbridge
o one reinforced concrete box culvert stream underpass
o one unusual concrete arch bridge across a two track main-line railway (Fig. 65).

● The road surfacing may be flexible or concrete.

Fig. 65. *Concrete arch road-over-rail bridge, showing erection of steel arch forms, second case study*

- 92 weeks available.

- Contract documentation appears to follow usual format.

- Nothing outside the contractor's experience except the concrete arch bridge.

- No obvious unusual risks.

Early decisions

The planner had been asked to prepare a plan to be used initially as a tender plan but containing sufficient detail for use as a working programme if the bid was successful. The planner decided that the three bridges and the tie-ins at the two ends would each need their own detailed plan, but the overall project plan should be presented as a linear programme. The early decisions made were:

- Who is the plan for? The contractor's construction team (albeit the estimator will make use of it first).

- What is the time-scale? Construction period only, 92 weeks.

Table 22. Estimate of planning time for second case study

Activity	Time: days
Make detailed appraisal of contract documents	4
Prepare three bridge programmes: use computer to analyse	6
Draw linear programme	5
Plan tie-in construction in bar chart format	1
Allow for conferences	2
Site visit	1
Total	19

- What is the level of detail? Medium, use a week unit.

- What planning techniques are to be used? Network analysis for three bridges; simple bar charts for the two tie-ins; linear programme for the overall plan.

Programme

The planner's estimate of planning time was four weeks, and the breakdown of this figure is given in Table 22. To complete the plan in the time available it was necessary to use three planners one dealing with overall plan and roadworks, another with the structures and the third planner with the traffic management at tie-ins.

Fig. 66. Concrete train, second case study

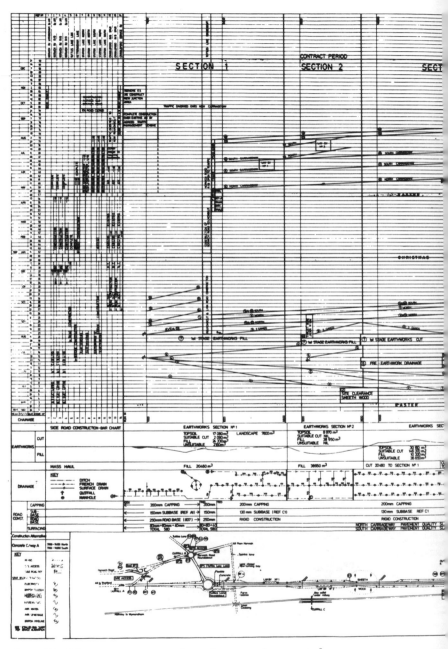

Fig. 67. Linear programme chart for second case study

138

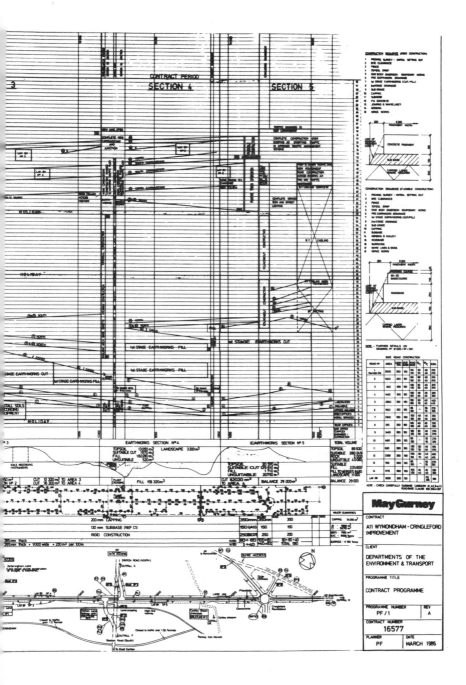

Detailed appraisals

A detailed appraisal of the documents was made. Lack of space does not allow reproduction of the detailed appraisal here but all comments of significance to the plan were transferred to the linear programme.

The planning process

For the overall plan the planner followed the process described in section 3.6. All information from the drawings concerning earthworks, drainage and road construction was transferred onto the lower third of the programme sheet. In addition a diagrammatic continuous sketch of the project was drawn at the bottom of the sheet. This sketch was annotated to show permitted accesses, side road closures and major watercourses.

Concurrent with this exercise, individual programmes were drawn up for each of the three major structures. No attempt was made to relate one structure to another or to the overall plan. Each structure was planned for completion on the basis of the most economic solution.

The next step was to decide whether the carriageway would be rigid or flexible. After much deliberation, the estimating team came to the conclusion that a rigid (concrete) road was likely to give the most competitive bid. With this information the planner could begin to construct the linear programme.

Planning was carried out as follows.

- The three weeks of annual construction industry holiday was blocked in.

- Before plotting earthworks, time was allowed for setting out, services diversions and soils instrumentation.

- First stage earthworks was plotted within the April–September earthworks weather window.

- The concrete carriageway was plotted within the April–October concrete road weather window in the following year (Fig. 66).

- The three structure programmes were plotted in simplified form on the linear programme as vertical columns such that the concrete train could pass all the structures without impediment, and continuity of work for craftsmen and formwork was achieved when possible.

- All the remaining activities were filled-in within the remaining spaces available.

The completed plan is shown in Fig. 67.

7.3. Network analysis case study
Project: Raw water pumping station and ancillary works
Title: Costessey Raw Water Transfer Scheme
Client: Anglian Water
Planning brief: Contractor's tender plan

Description

The project provides a new flexible raw water source for a quarter of a million people in the city of Norwich and the surrounding area. The project makes use of three former gravel pits that naturally offered an ideal configuration of storage lagoons. The scheme involves the construction of a new river intake on the River

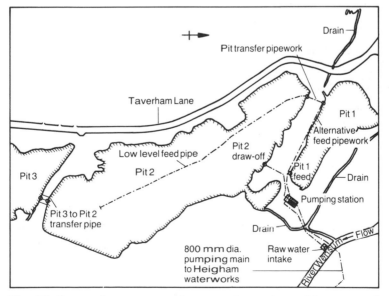

Fig. 68. Storage lagoons, transfer pumping station and interconnecting pipework, third case study

141

Wensum, interconnecting pipework to the pits and a transfer pumping station (Fig. 68).

The intake is sited on the south bank of the river and uses sheet piles with a reinforced concrete capping beam to accommodate a 1200 mm dia. steel pipe to transfer water, via the pumping station, to the pits. The low level pumping station has a reinforced concrete basement founded on chalk 9 m below ground level and water table. It houses two sets of pumps, one to transfer water from the river to the pits, the other to abstract from the pits and pump to the treatment works (Fig. 69).

1200 and 1000 mm dia. interconnecting pipework between the pits gives maximum flexibility of use in the event of pollution of any or all of the pits or of the river. Water from pit 1 is normally fed by low level feed pipe to pit 2, and water from pit 3 fed by interconnecting pipework to pit 2. From pit 2 the water is abstracted and pumped to the treatment works.

Planner's initial appraisal

The initial appraisal yielded the following major features

- the transfer pumping station will need to be constructed within a cofferdam 9 m deep

- deep well dewatering of the cofferdam will probably be necessary

- six intake structures are to be constructed

- seven sections of deep pumping main and pipework are to be laid, probably all in cofferdams

- the feed pipe to pit 2 is a site welded high density polypropylene (HDPE) pipe to be laid in a dredged channel on the lake bed (Fig. 70).

The contract conditions called for hand-over of the pumphouse for mechanical and electrical installation at week 7, with overall completion to be stated by the contractor between 75 and 80 weeks.

Early decisions

The planner had been asked to produce a tender plan to

- develop working methods

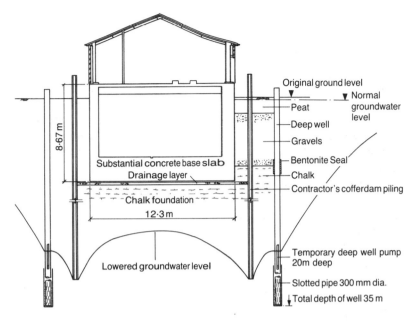

Fig. 69. Cross-section through transfer pumping station showing cofferdam and deep wells

- decide completion time

- evaluate site overhead costs

- establish plant and labour resources independently of the estimator.

The planner concluded that the project had a number of possible independent work sites, would need careful resource programming, particularly in respect of sheet piles and driving plant, and would require careful monitoring during construction. The early decisions were

- Who is the plan for? The contractor's tendering team.

- What is the time-scale? Construction period only, say 80 weeks.

- What is the level of detail? Medium, use a week unit.

- What planning technique? Network analysis using Hornet software.

143

Programme

The planner's estimate of the planning time is given in Table 23 and was 7 days.

Detailed appraisal

The following abstracts serve to illustrate the procedure used.

Conditions of Contract

Item	Comment
• ICE 5th Edition with Client's amendments and additions	Nothing unusual to allow for except Clause 13.
• Cl. 13. Requirement for contractor to enter Contract period on the Appendix to form of tender. Period may vary from 60 to 75 weeks.	Consider the risks, both in liquidated damages and inadequate recovery from preliminary bill items if project overruns.

Fig. 70. Fabricating and floating into position the HDPE feedpipe, third case study

Specification

- One way traffic system required for traffic on roads in site vicinity.

  Possibility of increased haulage costs. Need to provide and maintain signs.

- Any discharge of 'discoloured water' into gravel pits to be via settlement tanks and sand filters

  Many of the deep excavations will be within the chalk stratum. Need to estimate sufficient tank/lagoon capacity to still the chalk contaminated effluent.

- Mechanical and electrical contracts will run concurrently from week 59.

  Pumping station structure and suitable access to be available by this date.

- Noise. Pile driving restricted to 08.00–17.00 h Monday to Friday

  No contingency space for slow progress on piling works.

- Public access to the pits to be maintained.

  Possible fencing and signing implications.

- Excavation to the pumping station to be phased. Piezometer monitoring specified.

  Allow additional time in excavation period.

- No excavation to take place until sheet piling complete.

- Provisional sum allowed for deep well dewatering subject to the Engineer's instructions.

- River crossing must not reduce the cross-section of the channel by more than 50%.

- Dredging of a channel in pit 2 called for.

  Any floating plant used will need to be transported overland.

- Feed pipe to be made by welding HDPE pipe on site.

  Research previous job where this process was used.

Site investigation report

- Water table virtually at ground level.

- Fairly consistent layer of
  granular material overlying
  chalk with limited areas of peat
  in the top 2 m.

The planning process

After studying the drawings, appraising the other documents and visiting the site, the construction plan was worked out by means of a precedence network drawn in pencil on A3 graph paper. The project was found to divide into 11 work areas:

- the pumping station (Fig. 71)

- six feed or draw-off structures

- sundry other structures

- steel pipelines

- dredging and HDPE pipe

- external works.

Initially separate networks were drawn for each of these work areas with no attempt made to relate the networks to each other. By avoiding unnecessary detail, it was possible to limit the number of activities to an easily manageable number. For example, item 214 'construct pumping station walls: 50 days' could have been replaced by a number of items, one for each trade and each wall lift. Such detail would have cluttered the programme and inhibited the planner from getting to grips with the overall scheme.

Once all the sections had been programmed individually, con-

Table 23. Estimate of planning time for third case study

Activity	Time: days
Make detailed appraisal of contract documents	1
Site visit	½
Investigate methods, etc.	2
Draw network; time and resource activities	2
Input data and print results	½
Confer with tender team and reconcile resources	1
Total	7

Fig. 71. Transfer pumping station, third case study

struction logic and resource links were added. As many of the sections contained large elements of temporary work, particularly sheet piling, use of sheet piles and continuity of pile driving and extracting plant became significant.

The final network is shown in Fig. 72; it contains only 91 activities but exactly and economically charts the planner's proposals for building the project.

Analysis and output

Although the 91 activity network could have been analysed manually it was quicker and more cost effective to use a computer. The first analysis was carried out before resourcing the network and several adjustments made before the planner was satisfied that the best solution had been achieved within the contract time available. Part of the programme is shown in Fig. 73 in computer-plotted bar chart form. The format chosen for this illustration is very condensed with one week represented as a single unit of time. The software was also able to produce alternative, standard pro-grammes, using one day as a time unit. When the planner was

147

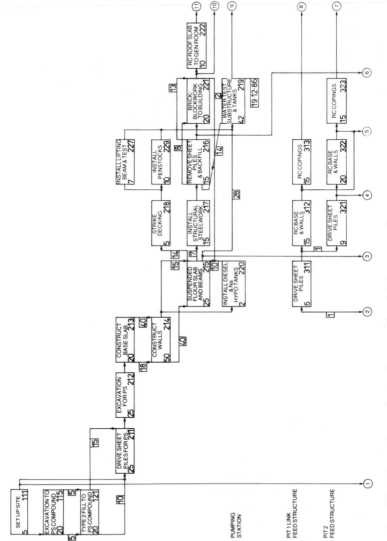

Fig. 72. Network analysis diagram for third case study

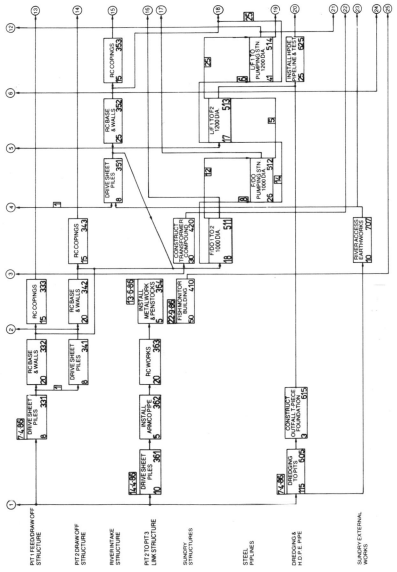

Fig. 72 — continued

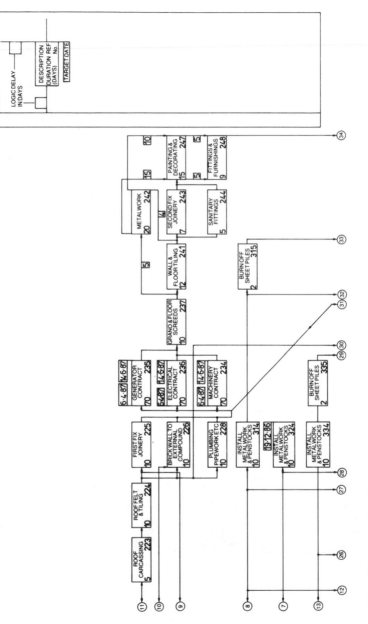

Fig. 72 — continued

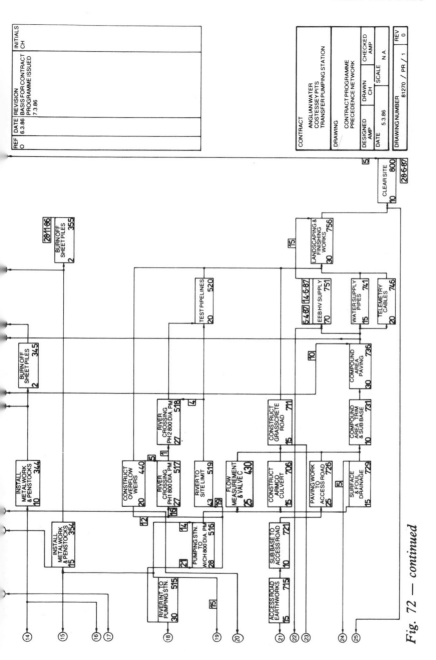

Fig. 72 — continued

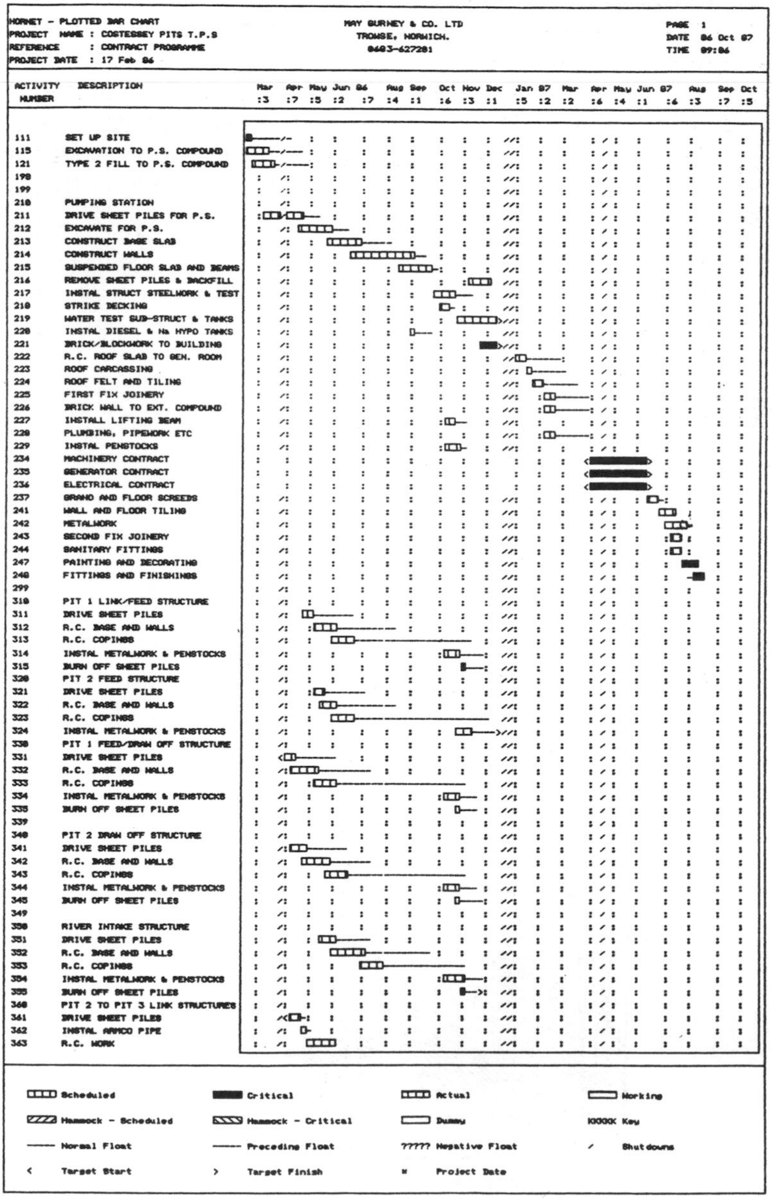

HORNET - PLOTTED BAR CHART
PROJECT NAME : COSTESSEY PITS T.P.S
REFERENCE : CONTRACT PROGRAMME
PROJECT DATE : 17 Feb 86

MAY GURNEY & CO. LTD
TROWSE, NORWICH.
0603-627281

PAGE 1
DATE 06 Oct 87
TIME 09:06

ACTIVITY NUMBER	DESCRIPTION	Mar :3	Apr :7	May :5	Jun :2	Jul :7	Aug :4	Sep :1	Oct :6	Nov :3	Dec :1	Jan 87 :5	Feb :2	Mar :2	Apr :6	May :4	Jun :1	Jul 87 :6	Aug :3	Sep :7	Oct :5
111	SET UP SITE																				
115	EXCAVATION TO P.S. COMPOUND																				
121	TYPE 2 FILL TO P.S. COMPOUND																				
198																					
199																					
210	PUMPING STATION																				
211	DRIVE SHEET PILES FOR P.S.																				
212	EXCAVATE FOR P.S.																				
213	CONSTRUCT BASE SLAB																				
214	CONSTRUCT WALLS																				
215	SUSPENDED FLOOR SLAB AND BEAMS																				
216	REMOVE SHEET PILES & BACKFILL																				
217	INSTAL STRUCT STEELWORK & TEST																				
218	STRIKE DECKING																				
219	WATER TEST SUB-STRUCT & TANKS																				
220	INSTAL DIESEL & Na HYPO TANKS																				
221	BRICK/BLOCKWORK TO BUILDING																				
222	R.C. ROOF SLAB TO GEN. ROOM																				
223	ROOF CARCASSING																				
224	ROOF FELT AND TILING																				
225	FIRST FIX JOINERY																				
226	BRICK WALL TO EXT. COMPOUND																				
227	INSTALL LIFTING BEAM																				
228	PLUMBING, PIPEWORK ETC																				
229	INSTAL PENSTOCKS																				
234	MACHINERY CONTRACT																				
235	GENERATOR CONTRACT																				
236	ELECTRICAL CONTRACT																				
237	GRANO AND FLOOR SCREEDS																				
241	WALL AND FLOOR TILING																				
242	METALWORK																				
243	SECOND FIX JOINERY																				
244	SANITARY FITTINGS																				
247	PAINTING AND DECORATING																				
248	FITTINGS AND FINISHINGS																				
299																					
310	PIT 1 LINK/FEED STRUCTURE																				
311	DRIVE SHEET PILES																				
312	R.C. BASE AND WALLS																				
313	R.C. COPINGS																				
314	INSTAL METALWORK & PENSTOCKS																				
315	BURN OFF SHEET PILES																				
320	PIT 2 FEED STRUCTURE																				
321	DRIVE SHEET PILES																				
322	R.C. BASE AND WALLS																				
323	R.C. COPINGS																				
324	INSTAL METALWORK & PENSTOCKS																				
330	PIT 1 FEED/DRAW OFF STRUCTURE																				
331	DRIVE SHEET PILES																				
332	R.C. BASE AND WALLS																				
333	R.C. COPINGS																				
334	INSTAL METALWORK & PENSTOCKS																				
335	BURN OFF SHEET PILES																				
339																					
340	PIT 2 DRAW OFF STRUCTURE																				
341	DRIVE SHEET PILES																				
342	R.C. BASE AND WALLS																				
343	R.C. COPINGS																				
344	INSTAL METALWORK & PENSTOCKS																				
345	BURN OFF SHEET PILES																				
349																					
350	RIVER INTAKE STRUCTURE																				
351	DRIVE SHEET PILES																				
352	R.C. BASE AND WALLS																				
353	R.C. COPINGS																				
354	INSTAL METAL/WORK & PENSTOCKS																				
355	BURN OFF SHEET PILES																				
360	PIT 2 TO PIT 3 LINK STRUCTURES																				
361	DRIVE SHEET PILES																				
362	INSTAL ARMCO PIPE																				
363	R.C. WORK																				

Scheduled · Critical · Actual · Working
Hammock - Scheduled · Hammock - Critical · Dummy · XXXXX Key
—— Normal Float · —— Preceding Float · ????? Negative Float · ／ Shutdowns
< Target Start · > Target Finish · ＊ Project Date

Fig. 73. Computer-plotted bar chart

satisfied with the overall structure of the plan, the network was resourced. In this case resourcing was done by calling up every activity on the computer screen and allocating resources. For this tender exercise it was decided that only three resources would be investigated: direct labour, subcontract labour, and cost.

The result of the labour resource analysis is shown in histogram

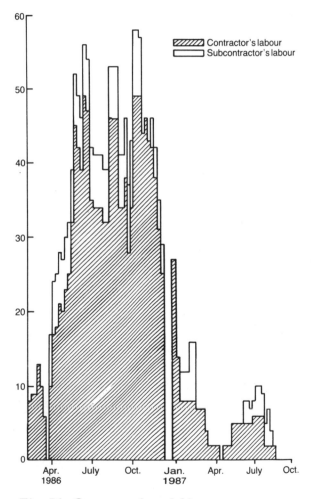

Fig. 74. Computer-plotted histogram

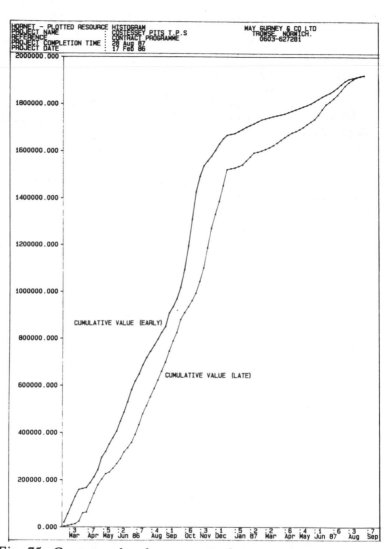

Fig. 75. Computer-plotted resource envelope

form in Fig. 74. Some useful estimating information can be deduced from this.

- There is an 8½ month period of high activity requiring an

154

average work force of 45 persons, of which 15 are likely to be subcontract labour.

- There is a 7½ month period of low activity requiring an average work force of only 6–10 persons.

Clearly there is scope for smoothing this rather indented histogram, but for tender purposes, the information is sufficient for contractors preliminary costs to be estimated, particularly those of site accommodation, supervision and personnel transport.

Figure 75 shows a computer-printed cumulative cost envelope derived from the cost resource input. This was available in the software package and enabled an estimate of cash flow limits to be provided to the client. This information was required to be provided with the tender.

References

1. *Wessex database for civil engineering.* Wessex (Electronic) Publishing Ltd.
2. *Spons civil engineering price book.* E&FN Spon, London.
3. *Laxtons national building price book.* Thomas Skinner Directories, East Grinstead.
(Although these three books do not normally list output data in a direct form, it may be deduced therefrom. Although these books are intended for estimators, and not ideal for most planning purposes, they can be very useful for timing specialist activities.)
4. Hall D. S. M. *Elements of estimating.* Batsford, London. (A sound introductory book to the skills of estimating. Although aimed mainly at the building industry the book is a useful source of data on output rates for labour, craftsmen and plant.)
5. Spence Geddes. *Estimating for building and civil engineering works.* Newnes-Butterworths, London. (Intended for civil engineering estimators but equally useful to planners, this book contains extensive output data for labour and plant engaged upon basic civil engineering operations.)
6. Caterpillar Tractor Co. *Caterpillar performance handbook.* Caterpillar Tractor Co., Peoria, IL, USA. (The classic reference book for calculating outputs of heavy earthmoving machinery. Available through Caterpillar dealers for their customers, or to be borrowed from colleagues.)
7. Price A. D. F. *et al. An evaluation of production output from construction labour and plant.* Available from Dr A. D. F. Price, Department of Civil Engineering, University of Technology, Loughborough, Leics LE11 3TU.
8. Neale R. H. and Raju B. Line-of-balance by spreadsheet. *Building Technology and Management*, Dec. 1988/Jan. 1989, Ascot, Berks.
9. British Standards Institution. *Use of network techniques in project management. Part 2. Guide to the use of graphical and estimating techniques; Part 3. Guide to the use of computers; Part 4. Guide to*

resource analysis and cost control. BSI, London, 1981, BS 6046.
10. Lester A. *Project planning and control.* Butterworths, London, 1982. (Written by a practising project manager with a major company, this book gives a very clear explanation of the subject, and is a source of much practical advice on the use of network analysis. Costing and computer systems are also included.)
11. Barton P. (ed.) *Information systems in construction management.* Batsford, London, 1985. (Contains some good papers on the subject by a number of experts. The papers cover a good range of topics.)

Bibliography

Antill J. M. and Woodhead R. *Critical path methods in construction practice*. John Wiley and Sons, New York, 1982, 3rd edn. (One of the best-selling textbooks on the subject, written by a practising engineer and a senior academic.)

Harris F. and McCaffer R. *Modern construction management*. Collins, London, 1983, 2nd edn. (One of the best-selling general textbooks on construction management. Planning techniques are included within a broad coverage of the subject.)

Harris R. B. *Precedence and arrow networking techniques for construction*. John Wiley and Sons, New York, 1978. (One of the classical books on network analysis, written by an eminent American professor. For a detailed and comprehensive explanation of the subject, this book is one of the best.)

Department of the Environment, Property Services Agency. *Planned progress monitoring*. PSA, London, 1980. (This booklet gives a clear review of the subject, with simple diagrams; available from the PSA, Lunar House, 40 Wellesley Road, Croydon, CR9 2EL.)

National Building Agency. *Programmed house building by line of balance*. NBA, undated. (Classical text on line-of-balance. Unfortunately, it is now out of print, but copies will be available from libraries.)

Pilcher R. *Project cost control in construction*. Collins, London, 1985. (A detailed and comprehensive analysis of cost control by an acknowledged expert. Includes cost control by both clients and contractors.)

Index

Activities, definition, 23
line-of-balance, 35, 36
Activity duration, definition, 23
line-of-balance, 36
BS 6046: 1981, 52
Balancing overheads and direct costs, 111–119
Bar chart, 23–24, 28–33, 34
standard sizes, 33
Cash-flow control curve, 96–98
Clause 14 programme, 13, 14, 88–89
Co-ordination, 5
Contract programme, 88–90
Contractor's control, 90–93
curves, 93, 95–96, 98–100
Control, 5
Control of risk, 85–87
Costs, definition, 23
Cumulative float envelope, 80, 82
Detailed appraisal of the plan, 108–109
Dynamic nature of projects, 121
Dynamic planning, 14
Estimating duration, seven steps, 20
Estimating programme duration, 15–17
Estimating resource requirements, 75–76

Event, definition, 23
Form of contract and risk, 87–88
Hierarchy of plans, 15
Initial appraisal of the plan, 105
Key activities and resources, 100
Level of detail, 10–15, 25–27
Line-of-balance, 23, 24, 26, 27, 33–43
analysis, 38–41
buffer times, 36–37
hand-over schedule, 42
monitoring, 100–101
parallel scheduling, 42
use of spreadsheet, 43
Linear programme, 23–24, 44–51
activities, 44–47
to networks, 51, 72–73
monitoring, 100–101
Linked bar chart, 29–30
Master plan, 14–15
Monitoring and control, 84–85
Monitoring bar chart, 30, 31
Network analysis, 23–25, 51–73
activities, 53–56
activity durations, 57–58
arrow form, 57
float, 61–65

hammocks, 68–69
overlapping, 67–68
ownership of float, 89
precedence form, 53–56
resources, 57–58
summaries, 68–69
time analysis, 58–61, 65–67
work method, 53–56
Networks, repetitive work,
  69–72
Objectives of planning, 4–5
Planner's tool-kit, 23–25
Planning techniques, anatomy,
  22–23
definition, 5–6
Planning, cost of, 8–9
data, 6–7
definition, 5
department, 6–7
in the organization, 6–7
saturation, 9
specialist, 7
time-scale, 15
Project manager's power to
  control, 3–4
Project time-scale, definition,
  23

Resource aggregation, 77–78
Resource analysis, 76–80
Resource levelling, 79–80
Resource scheduling systems,
  83
Resource scheduling, people
  management, 83
Resource smoothing, 78
Resources scheduling, 5
Resources, definition, 23
S-curves, 93–95
Selection of planning
  technique, 25–27
Senior management commit-
  ment, 1
Shaping the plan, 111–119
Subdivided bar chart, 30–33
Value, definition, 23
Variations and project control,
  119–120
Window into the project, 11,
  14
Work method, 23
line-of-balance, 36–37